THE ROMANCE OF
CANADIAN HISTORY

# CANADA 1

# YEARS &
# YEARS AGO

A Prehistory by
ROBERT MACDONALD

Book design E. W. Harrison


Printed and bound in Canada by
EVERGREEN PRESS LIMITED
Vancouver, British Columbia

# THE ROMANCE OF
# CANADIAN HISTORY

*Plate I. Precambrian Hills. The artistry of A. Y. Jackson, of the original Group of Seven.*

# Contents

# AUTHOR'S PREFACE

*The Romance of Canadian History* is presented not alone to chronicle the saga of a great and fair country, but hopefully in the interest of our national identity as well. It is nearly twelve years ago the series was conceived in the conviction that, as goes the interest of a people in their nation, and their knowledge of its trials and triumphs,—so goes its unity as a sovereign state. It must be true that to know *what brought about* an existing body of custom and environment is better to live in daily contact with it and with those who share it.

Certainly the need for this has not diminished in any way during those years. Canadians who know and understand the story of Canada need no struggle for ethnic, political or linguistic recognitions. They are not French and they are not English, nor are they American. They are not right, nor left of centre. All these characteristics they *have* and may cherish, but where their nationality is concerned they are *Canadians first,* and other things second.

The series does not aim to rival the works of scientists or academic historians. It seeks rather to offer a very human view of the events which have gathered over the eons and centuries, to culminate in to-day; in what we are and where we live.

This first phase, Canada's physical prehistory, has not been an easy subject to 'romanticise.' The historical interest of the people has not largely extended to earlier times than those of Man. And "Man" as an ancestor with whom we actively *relate,* has usually been seen as a creature who existed when his forebears reached the time of evolution from which archaeology has unearthed *weapons.* A primate capable of planning an instrument with which to slay another is instantly discernible as a fellow being; a kindred soul and as such part of our heritage.

But the story of the building of our country *before* the time of Man, *has* proven an exciting and fascinating one. And one which can impart a warm understanding of Nature to those who love the land, and would reach deeper into their ecology than the sensations and sights of the present. More, it is the *beginning* of the history of Canada.

Robert MacDonald,
Ballantrae
1970

# Prologue

*Plate II. Palaeontologists work to reconstruct a
Mesozoic Monster.*

# PROLOGUE

*Canada's written history and years of inhabitance by Man, are brief. But her physical account is as long and complex as that of any land on Earth. The past consists of historic time, in which we have kept records; and the prehistoric, in which we can only search: this book is a prehistory of our country.*

To understand the remote past, one must first shrug off his everyday concepts of time, and cease to think in terms of years or decades. His mind, unable to envision millions or billions of years, must at least *admit* that these eons lie behind us, and may well again lie before us. Only then may he perceive that the changes which have taken place in our land have been accomplished by the same forces he observes to-day,—*but in partnership with time.*

The fantastic, and seemingly limitless world of geology is itself an analogy in such perspectives. Imagine an ocean shore, looking out to sea in gathering dusk. The waves in the foreground are clear, much as the foreground of documented history and Man's short few thousand years of presence. But as your eyes strain to penetrate the gloom, the near and distinct are infinitely small compared with the vastness of the ocean beyond. Thus, shrouded in the dusk of the great spans of time are the secrets which tell the story of Canada's past.

Science has brought the record of the Phanerozoic Eon, which began some six hundred million years ago, to a state of at least 'asserted accuracy.' But the darkness increases as time regresses. And earlier, in the Proterozoic and Archaean eras of the Precambrian Eon, the knowledge which creates even educated theory gradually dims, then fades to total blackness, where our sciences grope endlessly for traces of the truth.

They work silently, and await further breakthroughs. And yet, the evidence now presented is entitled to respect. It has been compiled and correlated from an ever-increasing store of research, so vast as to stagger the imagination and far exceed the capacity of any one man. Slowly, with the efforts of many the great mass of fact is gathered, and pieces of the puzzle ever added, to form a picture at first misty, then growing sharper.

It is this picture that our prehistory presents, and to those who have devoted their years to this tremendous task, accords fully the credit of their findings. Our privilege has simply been to study their work, and assemble their triumphs.

The reader must understand that the accuracy of the facts and theories presented, and the story they tell, is relative to the extent of the secrets which have been unearthed to science. They are well founded and we believe them to be true. Yet, until we arrive at the threshold of *written* history, the principle of 'relative accuracy' must be kept in sight.

The theories of origin must be recognised as theories. And the history of the Precambrian Eon must also be so recognised, though here we begin to work with *findings,* and not with deduction alone.

We have reported from that store of fact and record now available. But those who would claim any victory over the enigmas of 'history that was buried,'—should also admit that much of it has not been dug up yet.

*Plate III. The Nebula, a whirling cloud of cosmic dust particles and gases.*

# THE DAWN OF TIME

*Years and years ago in a remote corner of one of the myriad galaxies in our Universe, there was born a small star. Nothing distinguished it from a billion others. The Sun's substance, formation and planetary satellites, were commonplace. But one of these satellites, the planet Earth, was to harbor the apparition and evolution of Life. And Life must include Nature's instincts of self-preservation: the will to live, to develop, to propagate itself and if intelligent to chronicle its history so that its passing will not be in vain.*

Thus our story might begin: and might brush aside the great eons of time, to resume when the first sub-human scratched rude pictures of his surroundings on the rocks; his instinct to create, and his desire to be remembered.

But Life is also curious. And Man seeks tirelessly his origin and the *cause* of his environment. He probes the hidden past, knowing that if ever he can fully define it,—he will hold the key to the future.

Throughout the years of recorded civilisation the many hypotheses of Earth's origin have come and gone. Each in its turn has been laid to rest by the advances of science. But each time the disproven beliefs have been replaced by new ones, each time based on a greater store of fact. Each time, a little closer to the truth.

The most accurate of the older theories, the nebular or, "single-body," hypothesis of the German philosopher Kant, was modified and published by 1796. It was later abandoned, and by the early part of this century most scientists had shifted their support to one of two, "second-body," theories. These stated that another star, passing near enough to the Sun to create tidal upheavals due to gravity, caused the expulsion of the materials which fell into orbit and became the planets.

Then, most of the varying beliefs were shaken. It had been discovered that many of the heavier elements in our solar system could only have been produced at temperatures *far in excess* of any known to exist in the Sun, or other ordinary stars.

To add to the destruction of the, "second body," theories, it was then found that the stars appeared to be of the same relative age as their planets.

More and more findings continued to indicate that *all* matter known to us, was originally in a single mass. And that at some point an unbelievable cataclysm had ripped it into millions of galaxies, billions of stars and solar systems.

Science was baffled. How else could an explanation be found, for the inconceivably high temperatures required to form some of our components? The answer, of course lay in the fact that the universe *is* much older than our solar system. And that the great disturbance, or 'big bang' as it were, *could* have taken place.

By 1946 new findings were published. There remained little doubt that the materials in the galaxies formed ten to thirteen billion years ago. And that the components of our planet did have a lengthy history, before they came together to create Earth.

*Plate IV. As the cloud rotates, gravity begins to mass the materials into centres.*

While there are still some exceptions who maintain the planetesimal or second-body origin, there has been a return to the theory of Kant in modified form. Science now generally accepts the nebular, or "dust-cloud," hypothesis. The planets and the Sun formed from the same cloud of dust particles and gases, at approximately the same time.

It is also well supported, that if we wish to state a, 'time of creation,' we may consider it to be in the order of four and one-half billion years ago, for the entire solar system. The oldest Earth rock dated so far, is 3.3 billion years old. The Moon rocks brought back, date at an average 3.6 billion, and these strata would have required a billion years or so, to form. Datings for fragments of comets and meteors are similar.

## The Nebular Theory of Origin

The nebula, a huge swirling cloud of gases and dust, was formed in space by gravitational accumulation. The same forces caused a concentration of the particles toward its centre as it whirled, and also toward smaller centres in the cloud's outer areas. As always in the law of gravity the larger masses grew at the expense of the smaller ones, until most of the material had collected in a centre body, the Sun, and in the several satellites that now swung in orbit around it. The heavier substances tended to condense first, and gravitate toward the centres. As the protosun and planets collected their material, the countless collisions of particles being pulled in created intense heat.

In the planets and their own smaller satellites the heat was given off at a greater rate than it was generated, allowing them to gradually cool and solidify. But in the Sun, the larger body, the heat accumulated much more rapidly than it could be dissipated. Its temperatures rose steadily, and as they mounted the star began to give off energy as well as heat. Now glowing and incandescent, it maintained its temperatures by burning certain of its elements, notably hydrogen, as fuel. It will do so for continued eons of time until the fuel supply is exhausted, and it begins to cool and die.

| EON | ERA | PERIOD | YEARS AGO | EPO |
|---|---|---|---|---|
| PHANEROZOIC 600,000,000 yrs. | CENOZOIC 67,000,000 yrs. | QUATERNARY 3,000,000 to 5,000,000 yrs. | 10,000 | REC |
| | | | 3,000,000 to 5,000,000 | PLEIST |
| | | TERTIARY 62,000,000 to 64,000,000 yrs. | 13,000,000 | |
| | | | 27,000,000 | |
| | | | 40,000,000 | |
| | MESOZOIC 173,000,000 yrs. | | 57,000,000 | |
| | | CRETACEOUS 73,000,000 yrs. | 67,000,000 | |
| | | JURASSIC 50,000,000 yrs. | 140,000,000 | |
| | | TRIASSIC 50,000,000 yrs. | 190,000,000 | |
| | PALAEOZOIC 360,000,000 yrs. | PERMIAN 45,000,000 yrs. | 240,000,000 | |
| | | PENNSYLVANIAN 30,000,000 yrs. | 285,000,000 | |
| | | MISSISSIPPIAN 35,000,000 yrs. | 315,000,000 | |
| | | DEVONIAN 50,000,000 yrs. | 350,000,000 | |
| | | SILURIAN 35,000,000 yrs. | 400,000,000 | |
| PRECAMBRIAN 3,900,000,000 yrs. | | ORDOVICIAN 70,000,000 yrs. | 435,000,000 | |
| | PROTEROZOIC 1,700,000,000 yrs. | CAMBRIAN 95,000,000 yrs. | 505,000,000 | |
| | ARCHAEAN 2,200,000,000 yrs. | | 600,000,000 | |
| | | | 800,000,000 | |
| | | | 2,300,000,000 | |
| | | | 3,500,000,000 | |
| | | | 4,500,000,000 | |

THE LIFE

# THE GEOLOGIC TIME SCALE

Geological time reference is divided into eons, eras, periods and epochs, just as our calendar time is graduated in millenia, centuries, years and months. But the time divisions of geology are not based on mathematics, with each segment being equal as in the calendar system. They are based on happenings, periods of distinct development, and obvious divisions in the nature of fossil and rock records. The five 'eras,' for example, distinctly differ in the fossils and evidences of Life that are found from each.

Figure I shows the divisions of time as they will be referred to in our story of prehistoric Canada, and some of the Life that dwelt in those times.

## Determining Age by Radioactivity

There are several methods in use to "date" rocks, fossils they contain and other samples such as skeleton remains. All work on the same principle; the transition of one substance into another at a known rate of speed. Uranium becomes lead, potassium becomes argon gas; the amount in which the one element is present in relation to the other tells how long the transition has been in process, and therefore how long the sample has existed. Both these methods have been used in determining Earth's age, and have produced almost identical results.

Carbon-14, the latest, most accurate (and expensive,) method, is on the mark within margins of 10% or less. It is used mostly in archaeology, on younger materials of ages up to 40-50,000 years.

"Relative" Age: is determined by the position in which a sample is found, and by the fossils in it. When both radiocarbon and relative dating can be applied to a given object, its age can often be told with a high degree of accuracy.

Figure I. The Geologic Time Scale

9

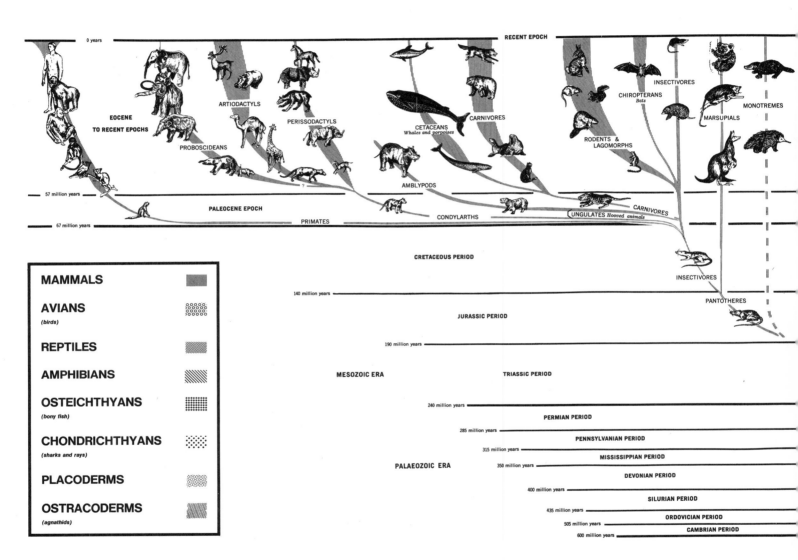

RECENT EPOCH

0 years

EOCENE
TO RECENT EPOCHS

ARTIODACTYLS

PERISSODACTYLS

PROBOSCIDEANS

CETACEANS
*Whales and porpoises*

CARNIVORES

CHIROPTERANS
*Bats*

INSECTIVORES

RODENTS &
LAGOMORPHS

MARSUPIALS

MONOTREMES

AMBLYPODS

?

57 million years

PALEOCENE EPOCH

CONDYLARTHS

CARNIVORES

UNGULATES *Hooved animals*

PRIMATES

67 million years

CRETACEOUS PERIOD

INSECTIVORES

140 million years

PANTOTHERES

JURASSIC PERIOD

190 million years

MESOZOIC ERA

TRIASSIC PERIOD

240 million years

PERMIAN PERIOD

285 million years

PENNSYLVANIAN PERIOD

315 million years

MISSISSIPPIAN PERIOD

PALAEOZOIC ERA

350 million years

DEVONIAN PERIOD

400 million years

SILURIAN PERIOD

435 million years

ORDOVICIAN PERIOD

505 million years

CAMBRIAN PERIOD

600 million years

MAMMALS

AVIANS
*(birds)*

REPTILES

AMPHIBIANS

OSTEICHTHYANS
*(bony fish)*

CHONDRICHTHYANS
*(sharks and rays)*

PLACODERMS

OSTRACODERMS
*(agnathids)*

*Figure II. History of the Chordates*

10

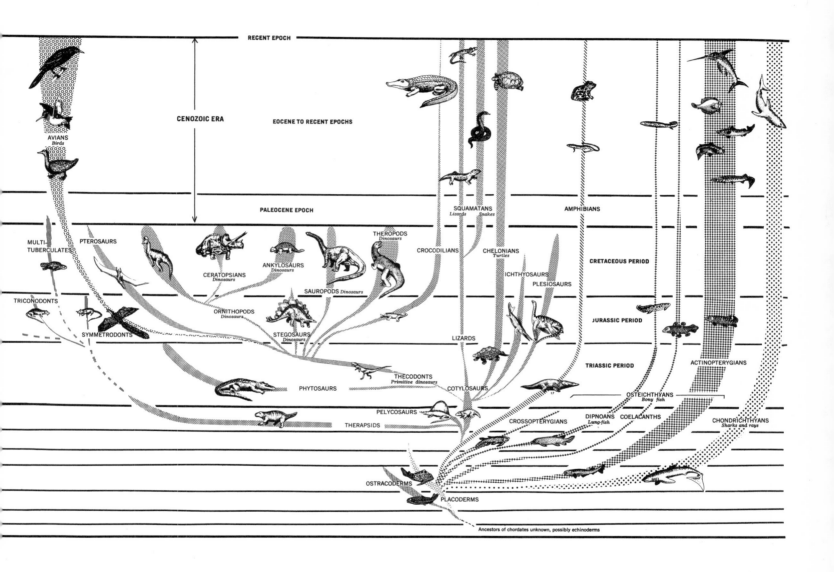

RECENT EPOCH

CENOZOIC ERA      EOCENE TO RECENT EPOCHS

AVIANS
*Birds*

PALEOCENE EPOCH

MULTI-
TUBERCULATES    PTEROSAURS         THEROPODS
*Dinosaurs*      SQUAMATANS
*Lizards Snakes*       AMPHIBIANS

CROCODILIANS       CHELONIANS
*Turtles*        CRETACEOUS PERIOD

CERATOPSIANS
*Dinosaurs*     ANKYLOSAURS
*Dinosaurs*

SAUROPODS *Dinosaurs*          ICHTHYOSAURS

PLESIOSAURS

TRICONODONTS       ORNITHOPODS
*Dinosaurs*          JURASSIC PERIOD

SYMMETRODONTS        STEGOSAURS
*Dinosaurs*         LIZARDS

TRIASSIC PERIOD       ACTINOPTERYGIANS

THECODONTS
*Primitive dinosaurs*     COTYLOSAURS

PHYTOSAURS                OSTEICHTHYANS
*Bony fish*

PELYCOSAURS           DIPNOANS   COELACANTHS
*Lung-fish*

THERAPSIDS        CROSSOPTERYGIANS       CHONDRICHTHYANS
*Sharks and rays*

OSTRACODERMS

PLACODERMS

Ancestors of chordates unknown, possibly echinoderms

11

# The Precambrian Eon

Plate V. Valley of the ten peaks, at Moraine Lake in Alberta.
These mountains did not form in relief until some fifty-seven
million years ago, but are almost entirely composed of
sandstones laid down in Precambrian and Early Cambrian
oceans.

# THE PRECAMBRIAN

*The Precambrian spans more than four-fifths of the time that Earth has existed; the four billion year total of the Archaean and Proterozoic Eras.*

The events of this staggering eon of time are as impressive as its very length. They include the formation of our entire environment, and the origin of Life itself.

The never-ending search for 'what happened,' has yielded enough to piece together an outline. Deep drillings in search of oil in the western plains have produced many of the answers. But in British Columbia and eastern Canada, particularly in mountain terrains, the Precambrian guards well her secrets, and there are great voids in the information we have.

It is widely accepted and follows closely with the theories of its origin, that Earth was molten until some 3,500,000,000 years ago.We know that cooling of the crust had taken place at that point, because there are sedimentary rocks almost that old.

For well over a billion years there probably was no Life. There is a near total absence of fossils in Precambrian rocks. Then, about two billion years ago the slim fossil record begins. A few are found of worms, corals, marine plants; the life forms were soft, and possessing no bone or shell structures, left few traces of their passing. But they were there, and their development required *time*. The earliest Life could have appeared at any time after Earth had cooled, and water could remain on its surface.

Precambrian rocks are mostly granitic. They lie beneath the younger strata in widespread parts of Canada, cropping out at the surface in some areas. In the Rogers Pass through the Selkirks, the Long Range of Newfoundland, in Northern Ontario and many other scenes of rugged beauty, Precambrian granites and marine rocks are part of to-day's land-

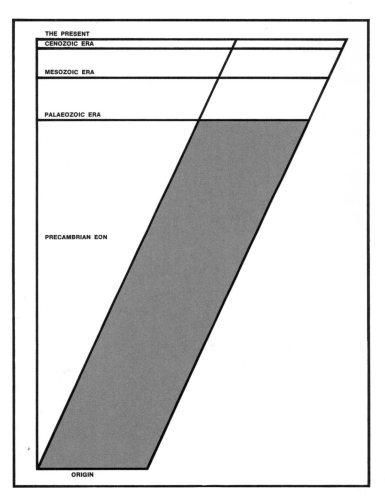

*Figure III*

scape. Most important of all to the structure of the land, they are the basic material of the Canadian Shield, great stable interior of the continent since Proterozoic Time.

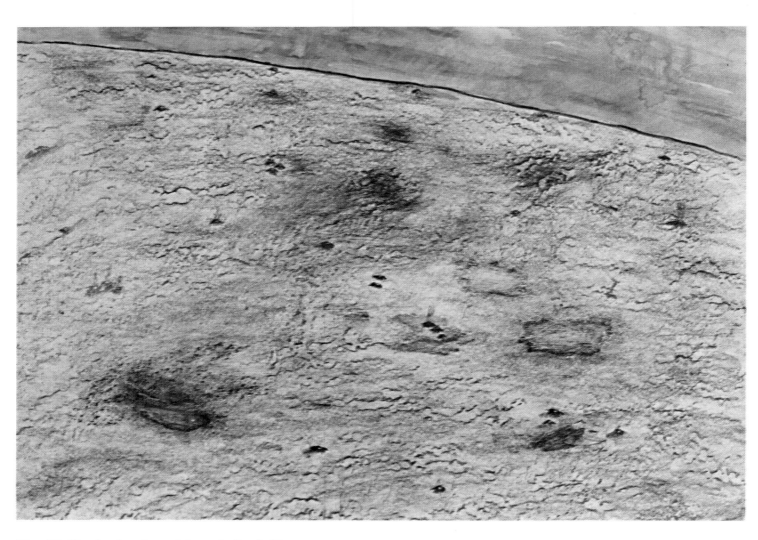

*Plate VI. Simulated surface of the early Earth. No*
*moisture or Life in any form could exist in its intense heat.*

# THE ARCHAEAN ERA
Origin to 2,300,000,000 B P

*(B P, Before Present. Refers always to years before 1950.)*

*Archaean, (ancient,) is the name given to about two and one-half billion years of earliest time in the Precambrian.*

The young Earth, thoroughly desolate, drifted in its endless orbit through space. The material-massing forces which had created its intense heat during formation, were spent. Now its temperatures dropped steadly with the passing years, and its crust thickened.

On the hot and arid surface, vast reaches of black basalt terrain glowed red in spots, here and there erupting white-hot lava. Patches of lighter granites and a few small volcanic mountains stood out against the black monotony of the plain. Earth, when it reached a diameter of two to three thousand miles, had retained an atmosphere. But its temperature was far too high to permit moisture in any form on the surface. Its 327,000,000 cubic miles of water were held in vapours, enveloping the planet in thick clouds.

When the cloud masses cooled to 374 degrees Centigrade, rain began to fall. Storms of unbelievable violence raged above the land, but the water could not reach the superheated Earth, evaporating as it came near.

The land grew still cooler, and finally water fell steaming on the rocks. It collected in the land depressions, seething oceans far above boiling point. Now the torrential rains poured down steadily. So great was the store of moisture in the clouds, that the deluge continued for an unknown number of years. In time, the water ceased to boil. Land masses and rocks jutted out of the oceans, the steady torrent ended, and the emerging landscape lay silent and lifeless in the first rays of the Sun.

The years wore on. Winds blew unrelentingly over the barren wasteland not covered by the primaeval seas. No plant life, nor any living thing, existed there to break the monotony of the elements constantly wearing at the land.

Crustal upheavals began, and Archaean rocks, the oldest known on Earth, were thrust-forced into great uplift belts. Where the Canadian Shield now exists, and in the far West, gigantic mountain ranges,—towering crags that would dwarf today's Rockies, stood sentinel over the plains and continental oceans. The present areas of the Shield are the roots of these giants. Long before the Cambrian, time and the elements would erase their majesty, grinding them to flat plains. And always their eroding sediments built the changing land.

## The First Life

It would be more than two billion years later in Devonian Time, that the first land dwelling creatures began their slow development towards the humanoid forms which would one day rule the planet. But here, far behind in the deep Archaean past lies the most dramatic single event in the history of Earth; their origin,—the appearance of Life.

Science offers more than one theory on the conditions that produced the first protoplasm or living organism, from which all others have developed. The theories have at least one common denominator: that Life results from the contemporaneous existence,—of the materials and environment needed to produce and maintain it. Life and water have many things in common. They exist almost within the same temperature range, 0 to 100 Centigrade or 32 to 212 Fahrenheit. Sea water has all the elements essential to Life; and the first living things were present only in the seas.

The earliest forms were so tiny and simple that they left no detectable fossil remains. But they lived and they functioned, and they were the beginning of all that was to follow.

17

*"In 1912 Alfred Wegener proposed that the continents had originated in the breakup of one supercontinent. His idea had not been widely accepted, but now evidence suggests that the principle is correct."*
—Wilson 1963.

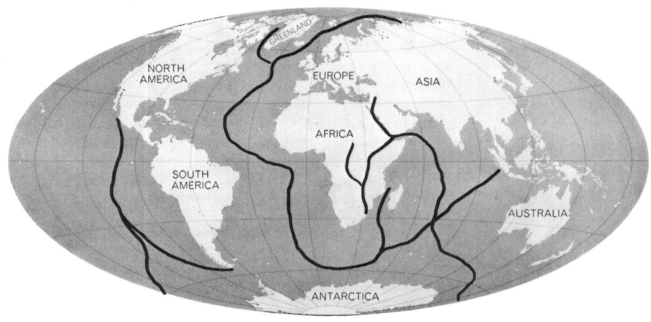

*Figure IV. The continents of to-day, showing the mid-ocean ridges.*

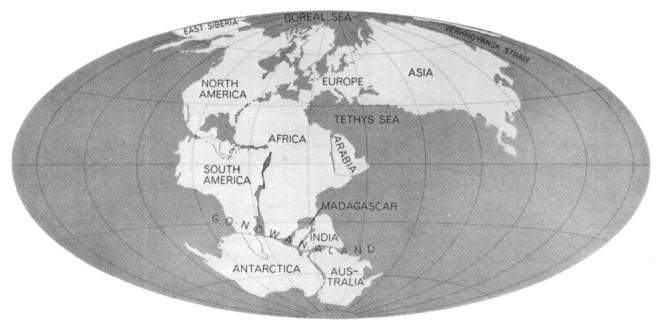

*Figure V. Estimated position of the Supercontinent Pangaea, about 200 million years ago.*

# THE SUPERCONTINENT PANGAEA

*Once, Canada was part of a single great continent. The Ancestral Pacific Ocean and the Supercontinent Pangaea occupied the entire Earth. Pangaea later broke up into Laurasia and Gondwanaland, which then separated further to form the continents of to-day.*

The theories of 'continental drift' and Pangaea have, by 1970 and earlier, become fully accepted by a great majority of Earth scientists. Findings of the last few years in particular, present overwhelming evidence that Pangaea did exist.

The jigsaw puzzle-like fit of the two sides of the Atlantic is of course the most tantalising factor. It motivated search for evidence of a one-time super-continent, almost as early as sufficient marine mapping was completed to show the picture of the coastlines.

There are many fossil affinities, from varying time periods and coastal areas. The Cambrian fossils of Newfoundland have European counterparts, and many relics of Ordovician time can be identified with those of similar dating found in Northern Europe. The first really *substantial* evidence of Pangaea comes from Cambrian and Devonian fossils, which have a *clear* affinity with those of Europe. They show that both land plants and fresh water creatures, either migrated freely or once occupied the same territory. And no rocks older than Upper Jurassic, (140,000,000 years,) have ever been found on floors or islands of the deep oceans.

The Caledonian Mountains of the Silurian Period, if traced from a point in Western Europe formed an arc through Scandinavia and Greenland, which continued in the Devonian-dated Acadian Range of North America. Then, later in the Permian Period the eastern ends of the old Acadian mountain system seemed to break off abruptly, while the remnants of the ancient Caledonian Range of Europe, where they faced the sea in Ireland, appear to have done the same. This may well have been the time of the first rifts in the land, before the separation which began in the following Mesozoic ages.

It is not evident that there was an Atlantic Coast until about the end of the Permian or later. The Gulf of Mexico may have existed before then, but prob-ably as an inland sea. Datings have been obtained that prove the Atlantic Ocean to be much younger than the Pacific.

There is a system of mid-ocean ridges in all of Earth's major seas, showing clearly the directions in which drift has taken place. Islands and marine rocks increase in age with distance from the middle. And explorations of the ocean floors have shown that they are steadily spreading away from the centre ridges; that the continents are moving apart at the rate of a few inches each year, and have been doing so for some two hundred million years.

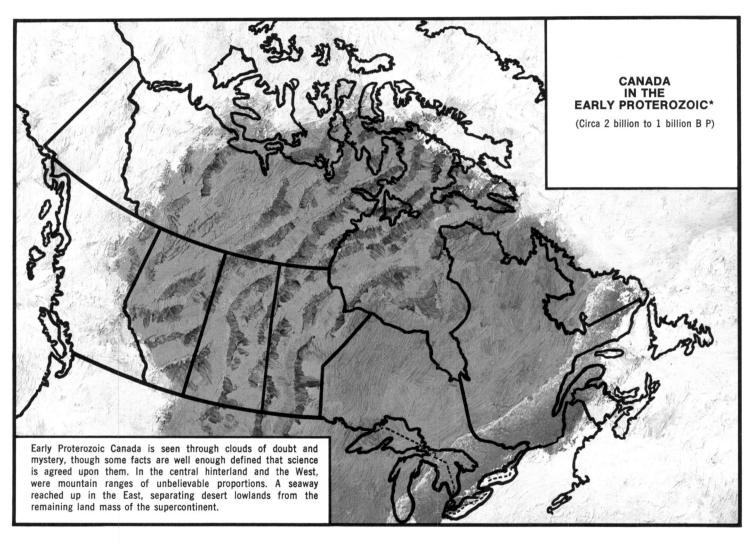

**CANADA
IN THE
EARLY PROTEROZOIC***

(Circa 2 billion to 1 billion B P)

Early Proterozoic Canada is seen through clouds of doubt and mystery, though some facts are well enough defined that science is agreed upon them. In the central hinterland and the West, were mountain ranges of unbelievable proportions. A seaway reached up in the East, separating desert lowlands from the remaining land mass of the supercontinent.

*Plate VII.*

*The series of palaeogeographic maps in this volume are from original oil paintings by Robert Dene Lacey, in the Ballantrae palaeontology collection. Photographed through an outline map of present-day Canada, they are intended to simulate a long-range aerial view of the country as it might have appeared, in each of the time intervals represented.*

# THE PROTEROZOIC ERA

## 2,300,000,000 to 600,000,000 B P

*1,700,000,000 years of violent transition and slow development mark the long passing of the Proterozoic Era. The Pacific Ocean covered almost all of British Columbia, surging against its coast where the highest peaks now rise in the Canadian Rockies, along the Continental Divide. Far to the west lay a few small volcanic islands, and a vast wind-swept desert stretched eastward, its shifting sand dunes dotting the great plains.*

The climates of the age at many intervals may have been similar to those of to-day. But seventeen hundred million years is a long time, and saw the passing of numerous contrasting changes. Extended periods were hot and dry, and desert conditions prevailed. But early in the era came the first known glaciation, when an ice sheet lay over thousands of square miles of Central Canada.

The first fossils that can be identified are of humble and primitive creatures from the Proterozoic. Though the soft-bodied forms left few signatures, the seas teemed with both animal and plant life. Those that can be traced include corals and algae, as well as worms, sponges and jellyfish; but there must have been a multitude of others that left no record in the rocks.

The building of our land and resources was on a truly grand scale. Ocean sediments in British Columbia piled up to eight and ten miles in thickness. On the northern plains and tundra, heavy metal deposits were laid down in the Great Bear, Great Slave and Lake Athabasca Country, including the Uranium discovered in 1930 at Great Bear Lake. In the East the old Algoman Mountains crumbled away, there was a time of intense vulcanism, and mineral stores among the richest on Earth were created; the great iron ore reserves of the Lake Superior Region, the silver and other metals at Cobalt. And near Sudbury, as well as copper and platinum, much of the world's nickel supply was stored in an area not forty miles by twenty.

Great mountain ranges in the West rose and were worn flat, many times during the Proterozoic. Again and again the combined forces of time and Nature built them, and repeatedly the same forces levelled them to the surface.

The old East Kootenay Range came and went, rising out of the ocean to dominate Southern British Columbia for millions of years. In the Canadian Shield, the close of the era again saw intensive mountain building forces at work. A huge range formed in Central Labrador, and another where the waters of James and Hudson's Bay stand to-day. The early majesty of the Laurentians was created; and the low hills at Killarney on the north shore of Lake Huron now, are the remnants of the once-mighty Killarney Mountains which covered the Great Lakes Region, stretching more than eight hundred miles from Wisconsin to the Ottawa Valley.

In the West, the sediments accumulating since earliest time had collected to immense depths. Now, the Cordilleran Geosyncline took shape. From Utah to the Yukon the great trough subsided, to slowly hoard for over a billion years more the materials which would later push skyward to create the Canadian Rockies, and the Selkirk and Purcell Ranges.

Only a handful of the profusion of events in the Proterozoic are really known to us. It blanketed a span of years almost three times the combined duration of all those to follow, bringing to a close the long and turbulent age of Precambrian history.

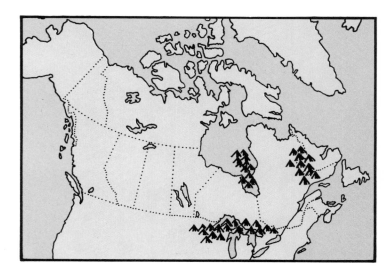

*Figure VI. Killarney range and other mountains in the East, late in the Proterozoic, shown on present-day map of Canada.*

# The Palaeozoic Era

THE  PALAEOZOIC

THE  CAMBRIAN  PERIOD

THE  ORDOVICIAN  PERIOD

THE  SILURIAN  PERIOD

THE  DEVONIAN  PERIOD

THE  MISSISSIPPIAN  PERIOD

THE  PENNSYLVANIAN  PERIOD

THE  PERMIAN  PERIOD

# THE PALAEOZOIC

*The seven periods of the Palaeozoic, (Ancient Life,) occupy a time slot of some 360,000,000 years.*

A successsion of epeiric oceans flooded the interior of the continent. Time and again they encroached on the land, and each left its load of sedimentary debris. Practically every part of North America was covered by the seas at one time or another, and in at least one interval only the highest land formations lay above the waters.

Climates were temperate at times, but more often tropical and even equatorial. Earth's poles have shifted over the ages, and there was a period in the Palaeozoic when the Equator slanted through Western Canada.

The revolution of living things was dramatic and decisive. Varying plant forms, left by the seas, were transformed through the passing years into tropical forests. The myriad of tiny creatures and organisms from the Precambrian, now branched out into highly diversified and larger orders of Life. The first terrestrial animals adapted to land as amphibians, and by the Permian the earliest forerunners of the dinosaurs roamed a primitive Canadian wilderness.

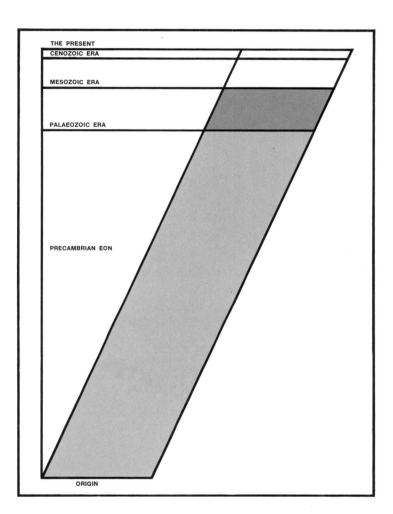

*Figure VII*

*Plate VIII. The structure of Mount Assiniboine, one of the most famous landmarks in the Canadian Rockies, is of Early Palaeozoic origin. Her rocks are the sediments of a Cambrian sea.*

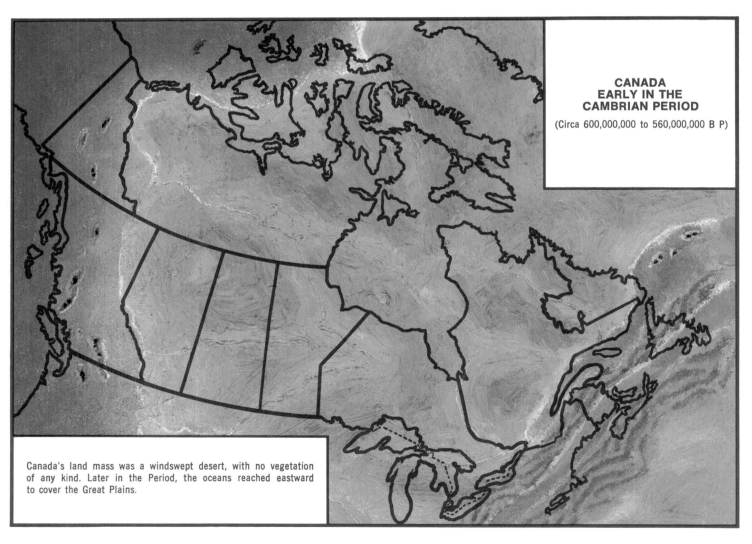

**CANADA
EARLY IN THE
CAMBRIAN PERIOD**

(Circa 600,000,000 to 560,000,000 B P)

Canada's land mass was a windswept desert, with no vegetation of any kind. Later in the Period, the oceans reached eastward to cover the Great Plains.

*Plate IX.*

26

# THE CAMBRIAN PERIOD
600,000,000 to 505,000,000 B P

*Six hundred million years ago as the Cambrian Period opened, there was little change from the land and climate conditions of the preceding Proterozoic. It seemed almost a time of rest; a long consolidation of the work that Nature had completed thus far, while wind and weather continued to wear incessantly at the land.*

The Canadian Shield was a vast region of low relief. Deserts still made up most of the landed areas of Canada, and the widespread indication of sand dune formations is suggestive of tireless winds. The seas over the prairies were shallow. Reaching eastward, they had moved into Saskatchewan by Mid-Cambrian, and late in the period had spread to Manitoba.

In the East, narrow oceans separated the Shield from the higher terrains of Acadia and Appalachia. The tip of a land mass called Montania, which appeared to the southwest, reached up into Southeastern British Columbia. Heavy depositing continued in the Cordilleran trough, and the old East Kootenays had long been worn below the waves. Volcanic islands still dotted the sea, far to the west near the present Pacific Coastline.

The period did not produce large quantities of minerals, and building stone is probably its most important legacy to the world of to-day. Some of the most typical outcrops of Cambrian surface rocks are found in Cape Breton, Eastern Newfoundland and in the Rockies. They are mostly sandstones, with some shales and limestones.

Life in the seas was profuse, and dominated by trilobites. Many creatures now began to form shells, and from this time forward left much more obvious fossil records. The small forms of the previous era were now joined by shellfish and early crustaceans, the forerunners of crabs and lobsters. Cephalopods, (squids and related marine animals,) first appeared in Cambrian seas and still exist to-day. They have through the ages varied as greatly in size as they do now, from tiny shelled miniatures to giant squid that may at times have rivalled the whales and great dinosaurs, for the distinction of "largest animal in history."

Though it appears to have been a quiet time, Cambrian waters and their sediments defined features of continental structure that lasted until Mesozoic Time.

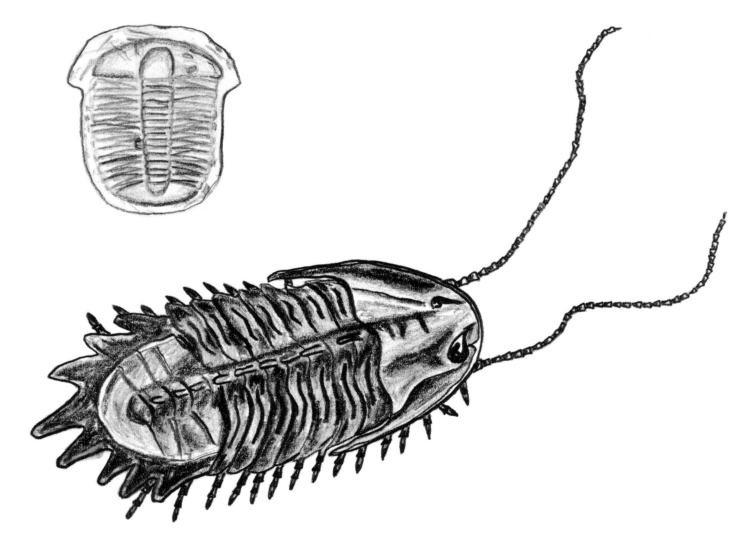

*Plate X. A Cambrian trilobite.*

*Plate XI. Cambrian marine life.*

*Plate XII. By the Cambrian, many creatures had developed shells or firm outer structures, and the clearly defined 'story of the fossils' had begun.*

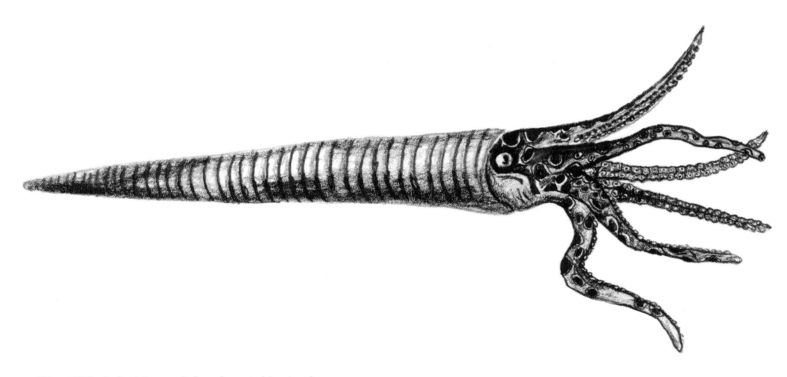

*Plate XIII. Ordovician cephalopods varied in size, but later developed to giant squid that may have been the largest animals in history.*

32

# THE ORDOVICIAN PERIOD
505,000,000 to 435,000,000 B P

*The climates were mild to equatorial, and marine life increased in size. Even in the Arctic, corals have been found which could have existed only in tropical waters. In Ordovician and Silurian Time, the north and south poles are believed to have been in Africa and the Phillipines, and the Equator in a position that took it across Western North America on a northeasterly angle.*

All the life forms of the Cambrian continued to flourish. The trilobite tribe had reached their climax of supremacy, cephalopods grew to lengths of fifteen feet, and now the ancestral corals arrived, adding bright colours to the underwater landscape. In the Ordovician seas the first chordates appeared; creatures with a flimsy structure that had not yet become a backbone. These were the ostracoderms, (earliest fishes,) a higher type of Life preparing for further evolution. Since all later Life developed from original marine creatures, they are said to be Man's oldest discernable ancestor.

Where the eastern coast of North America lies today, both the strata and fossils of the Ordovician appear to have required a continental connection with Africa and Europe, a baffling fact to geologists until recent times, when the existence of Pangaea has become widely accepted. The supercontinent did not break up until hundreds of millions of years later.

On the great plains of the West, the Cambrian sea drew back and left the land bare. The windswept desert that stretched east from the Cordilleran trough to Ontario, was still comprised of a Precambrian rock base, but now its upper surfaces were the deposits left in the middle and late Cambrian. There was heavy vulcanism, and the trough continued to fill with marine sediments and volcanic debris. In Southeastern Quebec mountains were building, and deep water still separated Appalachia from 'Laurentia,' the higher lands of the Canadian Shield.

Then the oceans again transgressed the land, and the close of the period witnessed the greatest flooding that North America has ever known. The Richmond Sea covered practically all of the continent. Only Appalachia, a few fragments of the Shield and the western mountain volcanoes, jutted above it in Canada.

The Ordovician contributions to scenery are many and colourful: bright red Queenston shales that are seen on the southern shores of Lake Ontario; rocks of the Lake Winnipeg Region, and the distinctive limestones near Kingston. Rocks in the Kootenay Lake and Salmo areas of British Columbia, and, perhaps most spectacular of all, in the grandeur of the Kicking Horse River Canyon where it winds through the tortuous miles east of Golden.

But the gifts to the future were being wrapped *beneath* the surface of the oceans; above them, the period closed as it had opened,—on a lifeless, lonely and desolate land.

Plate XV. 'Ordovician' rocks in the Churchill R. country.

Plate XIV. Ordovician marine life and sea-floor restoration.

35

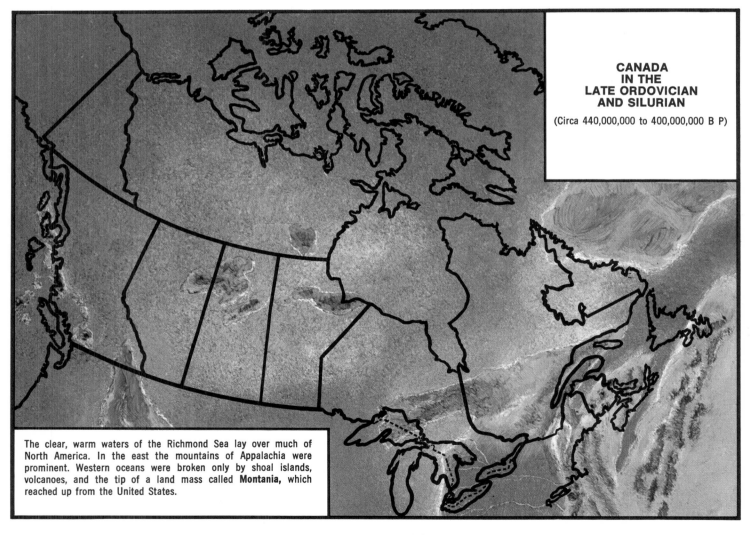

**CANADA
IN THE
LATE ORDOVICIAN
AND SILURIAN**

(Circa 440,000,000 to 400,000,000 B P)

The clear, warm waters of the Richmond Sea lay over much of North America. In the east the mountains of Appalachia were prominent. Western oceans were broken only by shoal islands, volcanoes, and the tip of a land mass called **Montania,** which reached up from the United States.

*Plate XVI.*

# THE SILURIAN PERIOD
435,000,000 to 400,000,000 B P

*The Richmond Sea lingered well into the Silurian, so vast that for a time there virtually was no Canada except for the Queenston Delta and the mountains of Appalachia in the East. Then it withdrew, to be followed by less severe floodings. The seas were shallow and clear, and filled with heavy saturations of lime. In other parts of the world as well as in Canada, Ordovician and Silurian oceans left the greatest limestone deposits in all of history.*

Small creatures built coral-like colonies from the lime content in the water, creating the origin of many rocks of the period. Placoderms now joined the earlier life forms, and the chordates, (jawless ostracoderm fishes,) became more numerous.

Life was changing. The trilobites had passed their peak, and their number declined. Corals and brachiopods multiplied tremendously, and sea scorpions reaching lengths of nine feet flourished in fresh waters. The ostracoderms probably began in this period to develop proto-air-breathing mechanisms, as Nature prepared for their destined venture on the land.

In Early Silurian the old Appalachian Mountains stood in high, rugged relief against the sky. By the time of the Niagaran Epoch, some twenty million years later, they had been worn to low hills. The influence of volcanoes continued in the West, and shoal islands rose intermittently on the plains. The northern tip of Montania again appeared in the south of British Columbia, while in the Maritimes, extreme vulcanism laid down thousands of feet of lavas and volcanic ash. Silurian terrain is present in the Rockies, prominent near Lake Winnipeg and in parts of Quebec and the Niagara Peninsula. The 'Tyndall' stone quarried in Manitoba is probably the best known example of rocks from the Richmond Sea. It contains millions of fossils, clearly visible, and has been widely used in Western Canada's public buildings.

The limestones of the Niagaran Sea are graphically exposed at Niagara. The falls were created by the water tumbling over a hard 'Lockport' dolomite layer at top, causing more rapid erosion of the softer 'Clinton' layer below. This happened only fourteen to fifteen thousand years ago, but the structural features are deposits that were placed there some 420,000,000 years before present.

In Late Silurian, an arm of the ocean lying over the Great Lakes Region became isolated from the open sea. The result was a 'dead sea,' a huge inland body of stagnant water that left deep deposits of salt and gypsum in Ontario and the Michigan Basin.

The period closed quietly, unmarked by any major upheavals or mountain building. But by its end, large areas of Canada were blanketed in limestone and dolomite,—another vital 'layer,' which would figure heavily in forming the land of to-day.

Plate XVIII. Tyndall limestone from the Richmond Sea, in Edmonton's provincial museum and archives.

Plate XVII. Restoration of Silurian ocean scene.

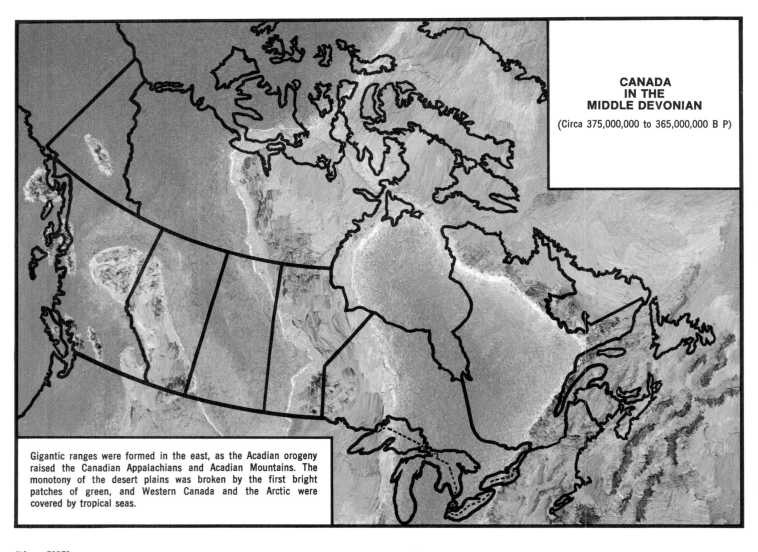

**CANADA
IN THE
MIDDLE DEVONIAN**

(Circa 375,000,000 to 365,000,000 B P)

Gigantic ranges were formed in the east, as the Acadian orogeny raised the Canadian Appalachians and Acadian Mountains. The monotony of the desert plains was broken by the first bright patches of green, and Western Canada and the Arctic were covered by tropical seas.

*Plate XIX.*

# THE DEVONIAN PERIOD
400,000,000 to 350,000,000 B P

*The Devonian is often called 'The Age of Fishes,' and the denizens of the oceans did attain vast numbers and great sizes during the period. But a far more dramatic set of events was taking place: plants adapted to land; and the first terrestrial creatures crawled out ow the slime to begin their long, slow evolution toward intelligent Life and—Man.*

Early in the Devonian, Appalachia became very low. Time and erosion had levelled her great mountains, and now gouged out a depression. An epeiric sea invaded this basin through the St. Lawrence Valley and extended itself westward, flooding much of Ontario and reaching to the Arctic north of Hudson's Bay. In the West almost all of the plains area was lifted out of the ocean, to once more become a great desert. Most of British Columbia was still under the Pacific.

Then, later in the period the shallow waters and coral reefs of the Elk Point Sea, reaching in from the Arctic, covered the prairies. Appalachia began to rise again, and its elevation continued for millions of years, culminating in the enormous mountain-making that produced the new Appalachian and Acadian Ranges. Again the interminable years ticked by, and the weathering of both ranges shed a steady flow of land-building materials into the seas to the west. Across the entire continent, volcanic activity continued with renewed force.

Devonian climates appear to have been highly diversified. There are indications of long seasonal rainfalls in the East, as predictable as to-day's Monsoons. Much of Western Canada was probably still equatorial.

The oceans were filled with a riot of colour; living corals grew in profusion, building huge reefs. Ammonoids and sharks had made their appearance. Fish grew to tremendous sizes. The 'placoderm' breed in particular approached the bulk of small whales, and jawbone fragments have been found near Exshaw, Alberta, of a monster that must have been thirty feet long. Still greater were the fierce armoured sharks, predators that were probably the largest animal of their time.

Abandoned by retreating waters, marine plant organisms took root on the land. Though small and insignificant, they were the food that lured the first amphibians from the abundance of the sea. The 'vertebrates,' creatures with skeletons, had developed, discarding their external armour for an inside framework which permitted much greater active movement. From the ostracoderms came the crossopterygians, fish with the first true air-breathing organs, and fins with bone structures which would later become legs. These four-legged 'tetrapods' may have been the initial land adventurers, but the Devonian also saw scorpions, spiders and the earliest known insects, take to the land.

*Plate XX. The growth and diversity of ocean creatures was profuse, and Devonian seas must have been an unbelievable panorama of variety and colour.*

43

*Plate XXI. Devonian armoured shark.*

*Plate XXII. Crossopterygian fish developed legs and lungs.*

44

The new land dwellers grew and branched out with passing generations, and the tiny original plant forms procreated forests of strange vegetation. There were giant seed ferns, leafless 'scale' trees and a variety of other flora, all slowly changing as they adapted to their new world. The West was still a bleak, uninviting and wind-scoured desert, but the 'Hamilton' shales of the East tell a very different story; their evidences of the earliest land forests have yielded tree stumps two and three feet in diameter. The wealth that the period left to us ranks high its importance in our structural history. Salts and gypsums were laid down in many areas. The fabulous beds of potash three to seven thousand feet under Saskatchewan were formed; one hundred and eighteen *billion* tons of it,—more than the known quantities elsewhere in the entire world. And fortunes have materialised 'overnight,' where many of Canada's vast western oil and gas reserves are found trapped in the buried reefs of Devonian seas.

The landscape legacy can be seen at the famous Percé Rock on Gaspé Peninsula, and in the rocks from Lake Manitoba across the plains to the Great Slave, La Ronge and Lake Athabasca. Widely found in the Rockies, Devonian rocks make up the 'Ancient Wall' near Jasper, the fossil beds at Seebe, and much of the scenery at Banff, including Norquay and Sulphur Mountains, the base of Rundle and the Palliser limestones of Mount Cascade.

Picture the Devonian Canada: the land is dotted by volcanoes, and swarms with scorpions and amphibians. Eastern swamps and forests stretch toward the crags of the frowning Appalachians. In the West the desert wastelands are broken by sparse vegetation in isolated green spots, and the tropical oceans are shoaled with coral reefs.

It was a scene at once primitive and inhospitable; but the land *could* support Life, and the sea's four billion year grip,—its absolute control of all living things, was broken.

Plate XXIII. Reef knolls on Bathurst Island, in the Arctic,
are from tropical Devonian seas.

46

*Plate XXIV. Devonian rocks make up the base of Mount Rundle, in the Canadian Rockies.*

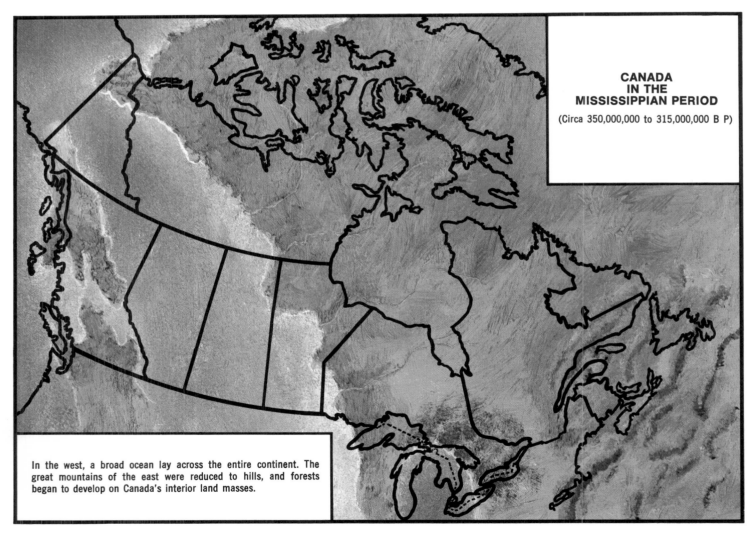

**CANADA
IN THE
MISSISSIPPIAN PERIOD**

(Circa 350,000,000 to 315,000,000 B P)

In the west, a broad ocean lay across the entire continent. The great mountains of the east were reduced to hills, and forests began to develop on Canada's interior land masses.

*Plate XXV.*

# THE MISSISSIPPIAN PERIOD
350,000,000 to 315,000,000 B P

*Three hundred and fifty million years ago the widespread oceans of the Mississippian Period were shallow, clear and warm. As in the Silurian, they blanketed millions of square miles with limestones. In Eastern Canada, from time to time there were large bodies of fresh water. The land masses began to take definition in the far West, and the seaway over the prairies stretched from the Arctic to Mexico.*

At the beginning of Mississippian time the mountains of Acadia, again worn low, looked over vast swamplands, and Southern Ontario was probably a land of forests and fresh water lakes. In the West, a broad continental ocean reached from south to north, inundating all of the prairies and Eastern British Columbia. Between lay the flat lowlands of the Canadian Shield.

The ancient Cariboo Range was formed on the Pacific Coast and interior, low mountains which are now buried under younger rocks and may never have risen to any impressive height. At the same time the ocean floors in B.C. were uplifted to create low land areas in the Southwest.

Mississippian rocks are rarely found in Eastern Canada. On the great plains they lie far underground, seldom cropping out at the surface. But, in the Rockies they are everywhere; the limestones piled up thousands of feet deep in the Cordilleran trough and can be seen in the ranges east of Jasper, in the Crowsnest Pass and in the upper strata of Banff's surrounding giants.

Late in the Mississippian the ocean over Saskatchewan and Manitoba was isolated, and became a 'dead sea'; there, as in Nova Scotia and Newfoundland, deep salt and gypsum deposits tell the story of great stagnant bodies of water, lifeless and steadily evaporating. As the period closed, mountains began to build again in the Southern Acadian Ranges. Vegetation grew taller and more dense, and with every passing century reached farther to cover the face of the changing land.

The climate was mild and marine life held its pace, changing little from the Devonian. Brachiopods, corals, fish and crinoids flourished. But out of the sea, as plant life gathered momentum and the food supply increased, the vertebrates continued their phenomenal growth. Amphibians were on the land, and their status as permanent residents well under way. True reptiles were emerging from many of the still-aquatic forms that preceded the coming explosion of Life.

*Plate XXVI. Mississippian coral in Dolomite.*

Plate XXVIII. A Mississippian Ammonoid.

Plate XXVII. Restoration of a Mississippian ocean floor. Crinoids are flower-like animals which became numerous in the Period.

*Plate XXIX. Rocks of the Mississippian 'Rundle Formation' form the upper strata of Mount Cascade.*

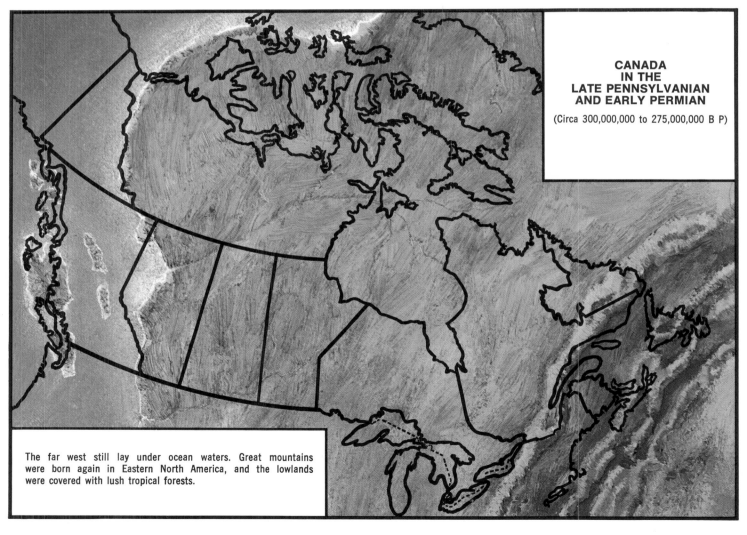

**CANADA
IN THE
LATE PENNSYLVANIAN
AND EARLY PERMIAN**

(Circa 300,000,000 to 275,000,000 B P)

The far west still lay under ocean waters. Great mountains were born again in Eastern North America, and the lowlands were covered with lush tropical forests.

*Plate XXX.*

54

# THE PENNSYLVANIAN PERIOD
315,000,000 to 285,000,000 B P

*The Pennsylvanian Period was a turning point, with profound and decisive effect on all Life to follow. It cultivated the enormous food supply that would make possible the development and growth of the great land dwellers, the saurians that were destined to supremacy on Earth for the next two million centuries.*

For the more than four billion years that passed before the Pennsylvanian, there had been only two 'land builders':—wind and water. The winds wore at the land. The water transported rock particles from the mountains and plains to the oceans, spreading them on the ocean floors to form future land masses. The elements were responsible for all shifting of substance, and therefore all change on Earth's surface.

Now, the burgeoning plant life brought another building agent into action; as the eastern forests reached jungle proportions, layer after layer of their organic remains piled up, creating peat bogs and swamp terrain. Compressed and stratified over the centuries, some became the heaviest coal deposits in history, where four-fifths of the coal fuel on Earth lay in beds as much as six miles deep. The legacy of the great forests lies mostly in the Northeastern United States, but Pennsylvanian coals are present in the Canadian Maritimes as well.

The West was still a barren wasteland with only sparse and scattered vegetation, and would be for another hundred million years. But even there, the advances made by plant life were significant. The seas withdrew again to the western boundaries of the great plains; and on the newly exposed desert, green began to appear in low-lying and moist areas.

While the plains remained hot and arid, the eastern climate was almost tropical, with heavy rainfalls. The Life responded with tremendous vitality. Fifty foot ferns were the 'underbrush'; calamites, scale trees and cordaites towered a hundred feet tall. Insects 'exploded,' many becoming over a foot in length. The land crawled with huge cockroaches, spiders, centipedes and scorpions, as might be expected in a sub-tropic environment. Dragonfly fossils have been found with wingspreads of more than thirty inches!

The amphibians now boasted almost a hundred species, ranging in size from a few inches to ten feet and more. Life in the seas remained for the most part unchanged, but on the land the earliest full-time reptile dwellers had developed.

*Plate XXXI. Pennsylvanian and Permian rock formations at Pavilion Lake, near Cache Creek, B.C.*

*Plate XXXII. Swamps and tropical forests in the east created the greatest coal deposits on Earth.*

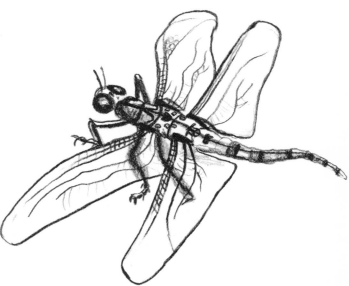

Plate XXXIV. Meganeuron a giant dragonfly of the Pennsylvanian.

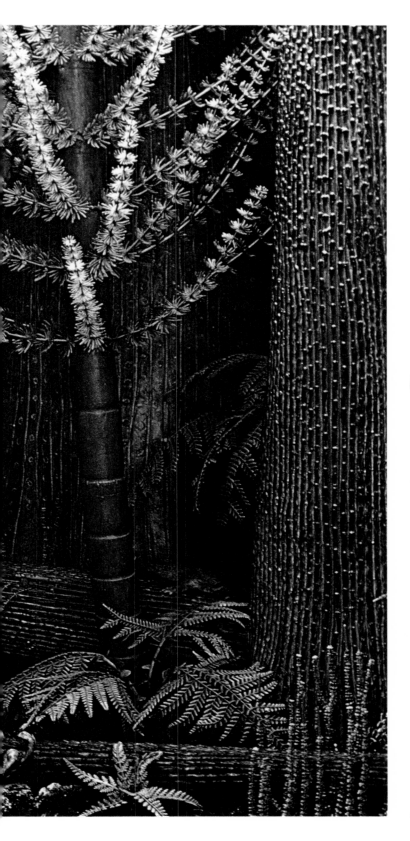

Plate XXXIII. Pennsylvanian forest scene.

Appalachia, early in the Pennsylvanian, had again been worn to low hills. Then, toward the close of the period, folding and thrusting brought the American Appalachian Ranges into being. They were mighty mountains, and are not impressive to-day only because some three hundred million years of weathering has once more reduced their stature as compared to the relatively young Canadian Rockies.

To the south and west of the Great Lakes Region, and in the far West lay the Pennsylvanian seas, now deeper than at any time since the Cambrian. The depositing of ocean-borne materials was prolific, reaching depths of up to four miles in parts of British Columbia. A volcanic archipelago continued along the west continental margin. To the south, soon only the Ancestral Rockies of Utah and Colorado remained as islands above the accumulating sediments.

Surface rocks from the Pennsylvanian and Permian are found on Vancouver Island, and in the Rockies they rest above the Mississippian 'Rundle' formations. They are exposed at the west end of Banff's low Tunnel Mountain, and in the country surrounding Cache Creek, B.C., particularly at Pavilion Lake where they tower as high as four thousand feet in sheer cliffs above the lake level.

The period closed on the phenomena it had created; a highly diversified continent of mountain volcanoes, deep oceans and burning desert, giant insects and massed vegetation,—a fantastic world of primitive Life and tropical wilderness.

*Plate XXXV. Restoration of Pennsylvanian marine life.*

# THE PERMIAN PERIOD
285,000,000 to 240,000,000 B P

*To the south of our borders, the Permian was one of the greatest mountain-making periods of all time. Heavy glaciation may have accompanied the forming of Eastern North America as it now exists. In the United States, further violence completed the Appalachian Mountain system created in the late Pennsylvanian. And extreme vulcanism in the West added to the general turbulence. It was a time of change, and of crisis for the living creatures on Earth.*

The movement and spread of oceans in the Permian, profoundly altered the mass of the continent. The great Phosphoria Sea stretched south and east from the Pacific margin. An inland sea that had existed in Lower Ontario receded, leaving a broad, flat plain adjoining the higher lands of the Canadian Shield.

Permian rocks, readily explored in Sundance Canyon and elsewhere in the Rockies, are found in areas almost identical to those of the Mississippian and Pennsylvanian, indicating that regions receiving ocean deposition remained fairly constant throughout the three periods.

Climates across Canada were unusually diverse; they ranged from tropic conditions in the eastern forest lands and hot, arid vulcanism in the West, to a major glaciation in the Maritimes, where the newly thrust-formed Appalachians must have been of tremendous proportions.

The first conifers had appeared in the forests, and may have developed in the West as early as the Devonian. Amphibians returned to the sea, or died off. The hardier strains joined the early land-dwelling reptiles, which now advanced to the initial stages of dinosaurs and reptilian mammals, though none of them reached the giant sizes that were to come. There was *Diplocaulus,* a small flesh-eater, *Dimetrodon* the 'sailfish' monster, and others resembling crocodiles and desert lizards. Plant life decreased sharply in both size and quantity, and insects became smaller though their variety increased.

*Plate XXXVI. Permian ocean-floor restoration.*

In the sea, however, there was an enigmatic and contrasting occurrence: the riddle of the great extinction that marks the close of the Palaeozoic Era. Many of the previously dominant life forms, the trilobites heading the list, vanished almost abruptly and forever from the face of the Earth. Others suffered decimation of their numbers, and the long-abundant corals became rare. The cause has never been discovered; climate changes, crustal disturbances and others, have been suggested, but the answer remains an unsolved mystery.

There was intense activity in the East. Another mystery, until wide acceptance of the existence of Pangaea, was the drift of the Permian glaciation, which was *south to north* though glaciers are known always to advance *toward* the Equator. Here in the Permian came the massive fracture of the Acadian Mountain system, and the contemporary break-off in the old Caledonian Range on the other side of the present Atlantic. And here, we believe lies the origin of the first deep rift in the Supercontinent, though the land masses did not undergo progressive separation until later in the Mesozoic.

The Permian ends the Palaeozoic Era, an age of foundation and formative drama. Life and the game of evolution were the top attractions, and the curtain would rise on the next major time division with a whole new set of players in possession of the stage.

*Plate XXXVII.* Diplocaulus, *a small amphibian flesh-eater.*

*Plate XXXVIII.* Dimetrodon, *one of the earliest reptiles of Permian Time.*

*Plate IXL. Permian rock structures at Bow Falls, Banff.*

# The Mesozoic Era

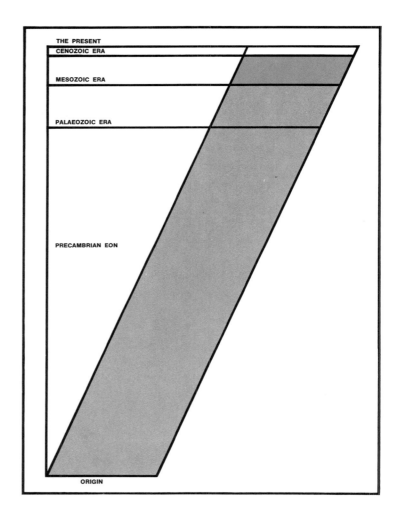

*Figure VIII.*

68

# THE MESOZOIC

In the Permian Period just ended, the marine animals which had enjoyed supremacy throughout the entire Palaeozoic had been suddenly and mysteriously wiped out. The trilobites and many of their contemporaries, were gone.

Now it was the day of the great saurians.* The "Age of Reptiles" had begun, and the dinosaurs, literally 'terrible lizards' of the Mesozoic ruled land, sea and air, as growth and evolution made them the most startling aggregation of fauna in history.

Like the most dominant of the life forms that preceded them, they were a doomed race. As they developed to the tremendous sizes that inspire disbelief in museum-goers to-day, they eventually took from the environment more than they contributed to it, and so their dying was a question only of time.

But Nature's balancing of the scales, like Man's justice, is slow if inexorable; and the procession of nightmarish monsters that dwelt in the Mesozoic had undisputed possession of Earth for almost two hundred million years.

Climates of the entire era appear to have been tropical at times, and by the Jurassic Period even the West was green.

The great north to south rift in the main land mass on Earth, had already appeared. During the Mesozoic the continents would begin to drift apart; first Pangaea, then Laurasia and Gondwanaland would break up, and the waters of the young Atlantic Ocean would become the eastern boundary of America.

*The record of reptilian development and supremacy is fairly clear in North America as a whole, but obscure in some ways as it applies to Canada. Many of the creatures referred to, have been traced only south of the 49th parallel. Also, in Canada the time of dinosaur inhabitance appears to have been heavily limited to the Cretaceous.

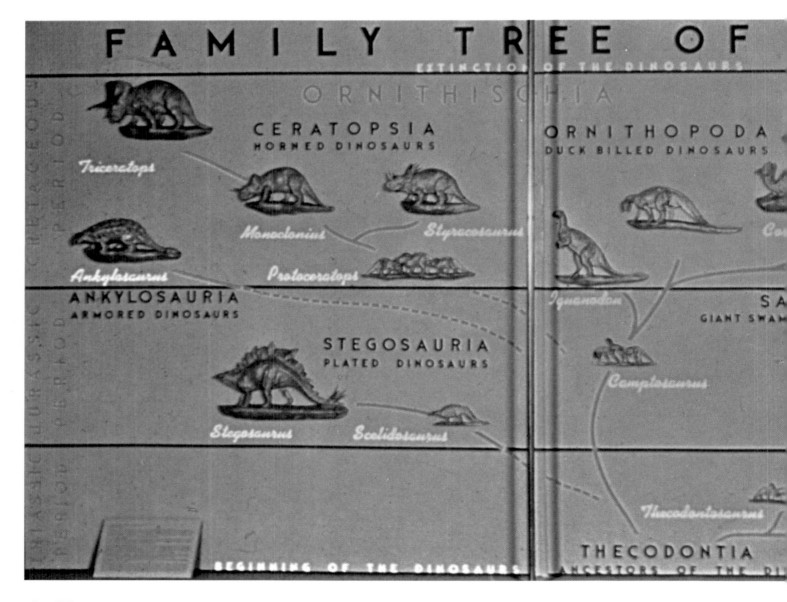

Plate XL.

THE DINOSAURS

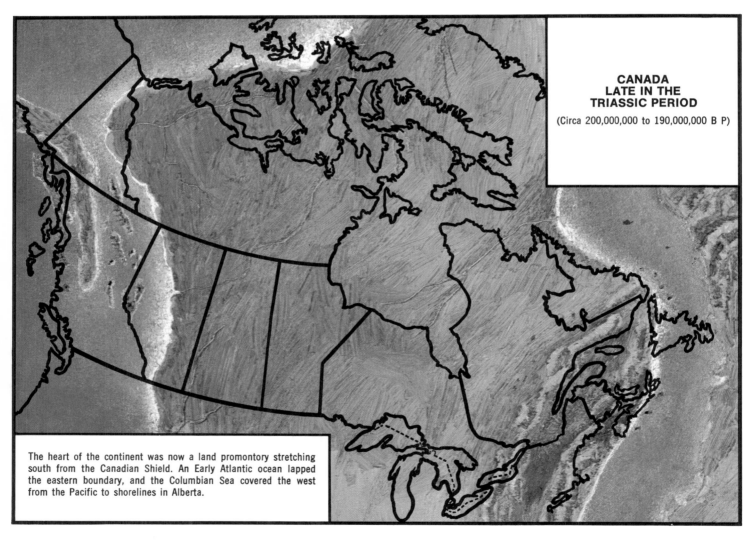

**CANADA
LATE IN THE
TRIASSIC PERIOD**

(Circa 200,000,000 to 190,000,000 B P)

The heart of the continent was now a land promontory stretching south from the Canadian Shield. An Early Atlantic ocean lapped the eastern boundary, and the Columbian Sea covered the west from the Pacific to shorelines in Alberta.

*Plate XLI.*

72

# THE TRIASSIC PERIOD
240,000,000 to 190,000,000 B P

*In the Triassic Period, intense vulcanism continued in the West. A rising corridor of land seemed now to reach from the Canadian Shield to present-day New Mexico and Arizona. The Ancestral Rockies still stood as islands to the south, in the great Wyoming Sea. The forming of Canada's Atlantic margin progressed further, and some volcanic activity appears to have been a factor there also. Most of Canada was now land, though at intervals the Columbian Sea covered broad areas in British Columbia, Alberta, Alaska and the Yukon.*

The climates moderated, and North American plant life again made gains in both size and territory. Plant types had changed markedly; the heavy forests of the East were now predominantly coniferous, resembling to-day's pines. The giant ferns, cordaites and other groups from the Pennsylvanian had almost disappeared, and redwoods, ginkgos, cycads and tree ferns stood in their place.

The great plains were still desert, but vegetation was spreading, and moist climatic conditions now began to reach westward. There appears to have been an eastern ice age in Triassic time, but its existence has not been proven; it may have been an extension of the Permian glaciation.

The old Cassiar Mountains rose in Northern British Columbia, then during the period eroded and were again covered by the Pacific Ocean. Lavas were heavily deposited in the West, and volcanic rock can be seen in many outcrops, particularly near Kamloops and Merritt. Triassic rocks lie two thousand feet thick under the Peace River Basin. And the main bulk of Vancouver Island is a variety of volcanic and other materials from the period.

Late in the Triassic, about two hundred million years ago, the separation from the single great continent appears to have taken place. Pressure from deep in the Earth was exerted upward and outward at the points of the present-day mid-ocean ridges; and North America began to inch slowly westward, forming the coastlines of the Atlantic Ocean and Gulf of Mexico.

In the seas, modern starfish and other crustaceans such as lobsters had now developed. Ichthyosaurs and plesiosaurs, the famous 'marine dinosaurs,' made their appearance to become the terror of the oceans, though they did not reach their giant proportions until the Jurassic.

*Plate XLII.* Phytosaurus, *and Triassic landscape.*

Turtles, reptile-mammals and the first flying reptiles were present in North America, and the dinosaur group branched to an ever-increasing array of sizes and forms. At first they were small, rarely over fifteen feet in length and mostly bipedal, running swiftly on powerful hind legs. The *thecodont,* a small bird-like reptile, was an agile, energetic carnivore, and ancestor of all the slow, cumbersome monsters to follow. Another of the earliest was the phytosaur, a reptile-dinosaur not unlike a large modern alligator.

The land dinosaurs of the Triassic were by no means impressive; but by the end of the period, they were well advanced toward the 'animated nightmares' of the remaining Mesozoic Era.

*Plate XLIII.* Thecodont, *ancestor of the great dinosaurs.*

*Plate XLIV. Earlier Mesozoic reptiles.*

74

*Plate XLV*. Edaphosaurus.

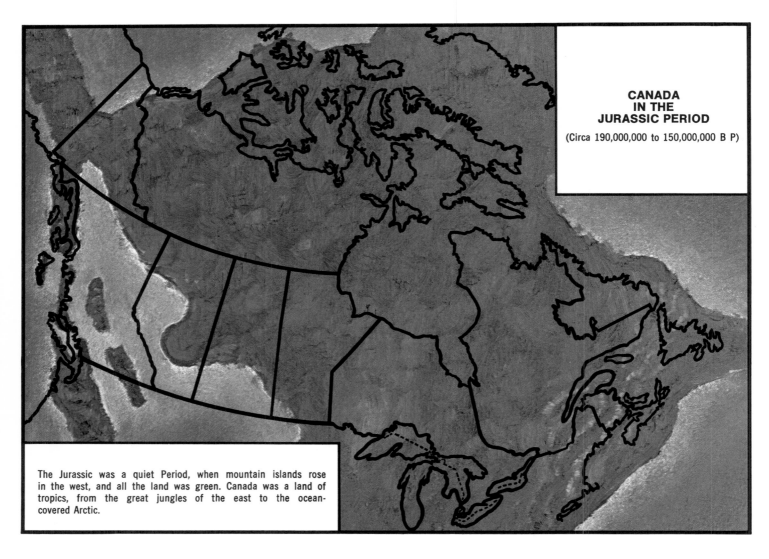

**CANADA
IN THE
JURASSIC PERIOD**

(Circa 190,000,000 to 150,000,000 B P)

The Jurassic was a quiet Period, when mountain islands rose in the west, and all the land was green. Canada was a land of tropics, from the great jungles of the east to the ocean-covered Arctic.

*Plate XLVI.*

76

# THE JURASSIC PERIOD
190,000,000 to 140,000,000 B P

*In the Jurassic Period for the first time in history, the West was green. For a time the Sundance Sea flooded the lower central plains from the south. Volcanic islands on the Pacific margin were densely forested, and many times spread their lavas into the surrounding ocean. Soon now the great dinosaurs would roam the famed Badlands of Alberta in the Red Deer Valley. Beyond the Rocky Mountain area the ranges of the Western Cordillera were formed, and warm tropical seas lay over the Canadian Arctic.*

The towering Appalachians created in the Palaeozoic were once again 'old mountains,' and time had reduced them to little more than prominent hills. The prairies, at first, were low and dry. There was constant vulcanism in the West, where land and sea were dotted with volcanoes from Alaska to California. Upheavals in British Columbia were forming the mountains of the interior, (the Western Cordillera,) and the disturbances of the period were responsible for the placing of most of the province's metal deposits.

Jurassic rocks are found extensively in the West, in layers up to twenty thousand feet thick. Under the southern plains lie deposits left there by the Sundance Sea, and the western mountains, coast, Rockies and foothills all shared in the buildup.

The climates turned damp and warmer; growth of vegetation was profuse all across Canada. Many areas became swampland, and even the Arctic was tropical. Much of the land was steaming jungle, infested with insects which now became small but numerous. Termites, flies, ants and grasshoppers had made their appearance. Butterflies and moths were probably also present; to-day they are dependant on flowering plants, and the first evidence of blossoms is found from the Jurassic.

An abundance of food in the seas gave rise to a new rallying of marine life. Sharks multiplied, and the waters teemed with skates, stingrays, herring and a multitude of modern fish forms. The air-breathing ocean reptiles, plesiosaurs, mososaurs and the giant ichthyosaurs, grew to lengths of forty feet and more. They were full acquatic meat-eaters, the ancestors of some swimming dinosaurs of eighty million years later.

Pterodactyls, (flying lizards,) and the first small mammals and birds were evolving from reptiles. And the dinosaurs themselves now included many of the familiar 'storybook monsters.' Some plant-eaters developed armour, against the vicious carnivores such as *Allosaurus*. Others, like the giant *Brontosaurus*, spent much of their lives in shallow water, both for protection and for partial support of their cumbersome weight.

*Plate XLVII. Jurassic marine life.*

*Plate XLVIII. Plesiosaurs, marine dinosaurs of the Jurassic.*

*Plate XLIX. Huge plant-eating dinosaurs of the Mesozoic were the largest vegetarians of all time.*

These huge creatures had surprisingly small brain cavities, and very little, if any intelligence; there was a tiny 'auxiliary brain' in their spinal columns, presumably to navigate the hind quarters, much like the rear steering gear in an old dual-control fire truck. *Brontosaurus* was sixty-five feet long and weighed some thirty tons. *Diplodocus,* a slimmer version, stretched ninety feet. And *Brachiosaurus,* the eighty-foot heavyweight, tipped the scales to an estimated hundred thousand pounds of monstrous stupidity. Bones of the brontosaurs have been widely found in Western North America. They became extinct about 130,000,000 years ago in the Early Cretaceous, unable to cope with the savage meat-eating saurians.

*Stegosaurus* was an armoured dinosaur, usually some twenty feet in length; he had a tail armed with spikes, and was one of the few plant-eaters able to protect himself from his enemies. *Ornitholestes* was one of the 'bird mimic' dinosaur types so plentiful in the Red Deer Valley Badlands. These small predators, because of their speed and ferocity, were even more destructive than the great, slow-moving carnivores.

By the end of the period almost all of Canada was land; the Sundance Sea had been the last of the great continental oceans. Never again, would vast areas of Canada be characterised by identical marine deposits and development. Now, each physical division of the country would begin its own distinctive formation, over the millions of years yet to come.

*Plate XLIX. Ichthyosaurs, appearing to be fish, were aquatic reptiles.*

CHAS. R. KNIGHT
JUNE 1902

*Plate LI. Stegosaurus.*

*Plate LII. Bird-mimic dinosaur,* Ornitholestes.

*Plate LIII. Armoured vegetarian of the Stegosaur type.*

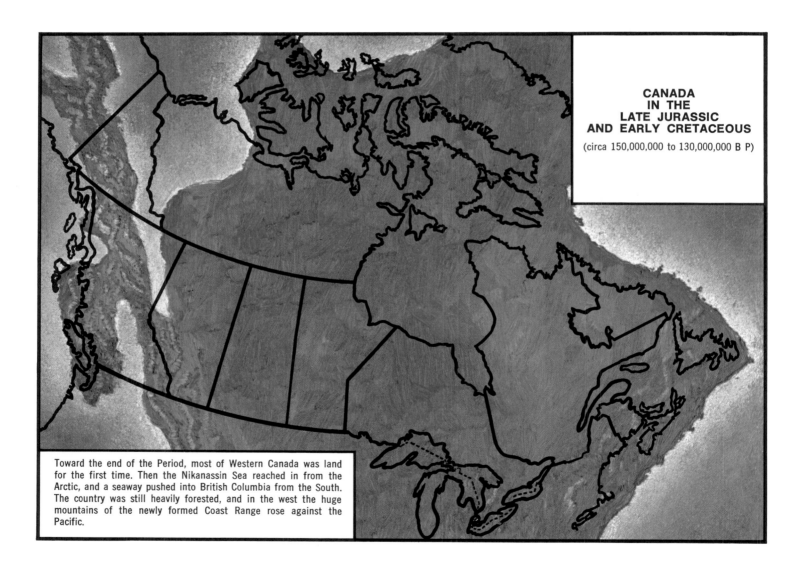

**CANADA
IN THE
LATE JURASSIC
AND EARLY CRETACEOUS**

(circa 150,000,000 to 130,000,000 B P)

Toward the end of the Period, most of Western Canada was land for the first time. Then the Nikanassin Sea reached in from the Arctic, and a seaway pushed into British Columbia from the South. The country was still heavily forested, and in the west the huge mountains of the newly formed Coast Range rose against the Pacific.

*Plate LV. Rock formations in the Badlands of Alberta, the famed 'Dinosaur Valley' created in the Late Jurassic and Cretaceous.*

# THE CRETACEOUS PERIOD
140,000,000 to 67,000,000 B P

*The Cordilleran ranges of the British Columbia interior, uplifted in the Jurassic, were completed in the Early Cretaceous. To imagine the stature of these mountains, it is only necessary to reflect that they have already undergone erosion for more than twice the present age of the Canadian Rockies. Parts of the land mass of Appalachia, dry terrain for some five hundred million years, now sank forever beneath the waves of the new Atlantic, as Canada's eastern coastline took shape. From sea to sea the land was green, and even the high country was covered by verdant jungle.*

The Canadian Shield continued to rise. Fully half of North America was submerged, but the dominant land masses were in Canada—the Shield, the East, the Cordillera, and now gradually the great western plains. Greenland, apparently till now a part of the Shield, was severed from it by a trough extending north to Disco Island. Later, it was further separated by drifting, or by downfaulting of land.

Volcanoes were still rampant in much of British Columbia and Alaska. The period is responsible for most of Western Canada's coal, and for the greatest oil and gas reserves in all of history. The tar sands that lie for over a hundred miles along the Athabasca River contain more petroleum than is known to exist elsewhere on Earth, an estimated three hundred *billion* barrels. The rocks are Cretaceous, but geologists recognise the possibility that the oil may also have seeped upward from reefs left by Devonian seas, almost three hundred million years earlier.

Much of the makeup of the Gulf Islands and Queen Charlottes is Cretaceous rock, and the Straits of Georgia were dry land for most of the period. Other areas of surface structure in Western Canada are too numerous to mention; the plains, Rockies, interior and coastal ranges, all were heavily affected by the deposition. About seventy-five million years ago the Red Deer River Valley Badlands of Alberta were carved out, and are known the world over for the dinosaur remains that are found there. In Horseshoe

*Plate LVI. Cretaceous rocks at Burnt Timber Creek, in the Southern Alberta Foothills.*

Canyon and other areas near Drumheller, more graphically than anywhere else in North America, the story of the great reptiles is written in the rocks.

Climates varied, often tropical; palms, cinnamon and fig trees grew, not only in Canada but as far north as Alaska and Greenland. Thousands of modern plants developed; grasses and flowering forms joined the lush vegetation, and giant redwoods stood in the forests. Insects had again increased in number, and swarmed freely over a land that knew no winter.

The Jurassic Period that passed before, saw the last of the great inland seas. Now came the time of the last epeiric oceans that would ever cover Western Canada.

Some time after 130,000,000 BP the Clearwater Sea reached south from the Arctic, to invade the upper central plains. It was active in the extreme, at times covering all of the prairies, then receding northward again. At the same time the waters lying over much of the United States occasionally extended north to submerge parts of Lower Alberta, Saskatchewan and Manitoba. Near the middle of the period these oceans joined to form a huge seaway called the Colorado Sea, which merged with the Gulf of Mexico, angling north to south a thousand miles wide across the entire continent.

Then the upper portion withdrew to the Arctic, leaving only the southern inundation on the plains. In the latter half of the Cretaceous this also drew back, and the land was dry. One final submergence took place as, late in the period, the Bearpaw Sea again flooded the prairies from the south. It was

expelled as the Shield continued to rise, and after a one and one-half billion year succession of oceans, the West had been under marine waters for the last time.

The acquatic reptiles of the Jurassic still lived, and remains have also been found of turtles that were twelve to fifteen feet in diameter. Otherwise, modern fish and crustaceans flourished, and Life in the seas began to look much as it does to-day.

True birds had now developed; the earliest appear to have been waterfowl types, which had teeth and lived on a diet of fish. One loon-like diving variety may have been six feet long. The pterosaurs, (or pterodactyls,) were not feathered birds, but flying reptile gliders with leathery, bat-like wings. They definitely lived in this period, though for some reason no Canadian finds have ever been made of their remains. *Pteranodon,* the largest of them, never strayed far from water. His skeleton fossils have been unearthed in Kansas, proving wingspans of almost thirty feet.

*Plate LVII. Cretaceous marine life, (ocean floor restoration.)*

*Plate LVIII. Giant sea turtles of the period.*

Snakes had made their earliest appearance. And now the first mammals, small rodent-like insectivores, began the evolution journey which would culminate in their own time of Earth supremacy. There is also some evidence of marsupials, pouch-bearing types such as the opossum. They were timid, defenseless and uninspiring little creatures, their inauspicious beginning almost unbelievable when viewed against the role destined to be played by their descendants.

Reptiles had reached the peak of their life cycle. The great plesiosaurs, (literally, 'sea dragons,') were supreme in the oceans, as the 'terrible lizards' were on the land, and may have grown to equal sizes. From earlier forms had developed large, swimming dinosaurs such as *Champosaurus;* the ornithopods, (Duck-billed dinosaurs,) were plant-eaters that spent most of their lives in the water. Mososaurs, forty foot streamlined reptiles that looked like fish, still terrorized the seas.

On land, many of the Jurassic forms still existed but had grown larger. Huge *Brontosaurus* had not survived; the stegosaurs had disappeared and been replaced with new armoured 'land tanks' like *Triceratops*. Saurichians, the small bird-mimic dinosaurs were present as before, and still the most common source of swift, savage death to the small animals. Theropods, the big carnivorous dinosaurs, roamed the land menacing all life in their path. *Gorgosaurus, (Albertosaurus,)* was the most common of this group in Canada. *Tyrannosaurus Rex* was the largest, and is probably the best known to museum-goers. *Rex* was not long on intelligence, but

Trachodon, *Cretaceous Ornithopod.*

Triceratops *model at Drumheller.*

*Plate LIX. Flying reptile Pterodactyls.*

*Plate LX.*

*Plate LXI.* Styracosaurus, *armoured vegetarian dinosaur.*

his fifty foot frame was easily Nature's ultimate engineering accomplishment—in sheer, destructive horror.

The close of the Cretaceous, end of the Mesozoic Era, marked history's second sweeping extinction. Of the land dinosaurs, marine and flying reptiles, few survived the Mesozoic, and the mammal kingdom began their ascent in earnest.

As in the case of the first mass wipeout at the end of the Palaeozoic, the forces that wrote the swan song of the great saurians are a complete and totally unsolved mystery. It would appear that the same influence also destroyed the countless billions of ammonites that inhabited the seas. The extinction has been attributed to many possible causes; changes in climatic or meteorological conditions, the possibility that they literally 'ate up their food supply,' the rise of the mammals, insects, disease and others have all been considered. The fact that they vanished first in the North may be significant. Another logical theory may be that a racial decadence, or 'senility of species' had set in; they were, after all, a genetic series almost two hundred million years old.

Whatever the physical factors, one statement of cause is certain: that again a dominant life group had outgrown its environment, and had upset Nature's balance; Nature countered as She always has done,—by exacting payment in full.

*Plate LXII.* Albertosaurus, *(Gorgosaur,) of the Red Deer Valley Badlands.*

*Plate LXIII. Theropod carnivores.*

*Plate LXIV.* Tyrannosaurus Rex.

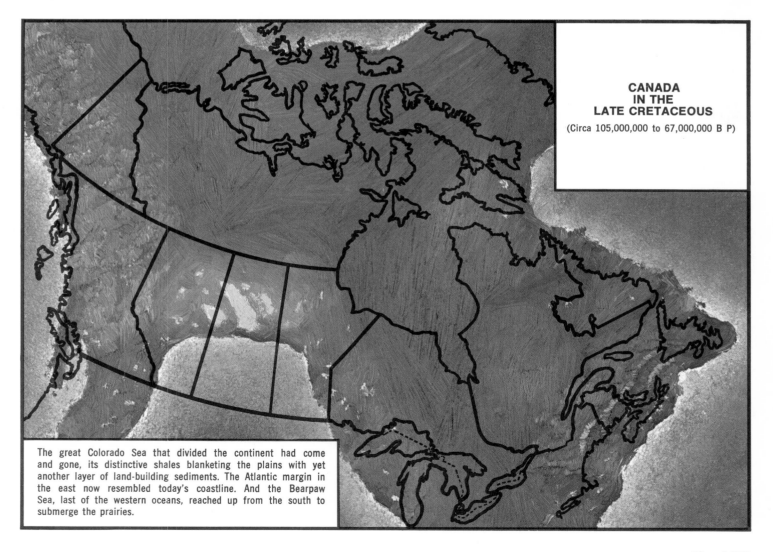

**CANADA
IN THE
LATE CRETACEOUS**

(Circa 105,000,000 to 67,000,000 B P)

The great Colorado Sea that divided the continent had come and gone, its distinctive shales blanketing the plains with yet another layer of land-building sediments. The Atlantic margin in the east now resembled today's coastline. And the Bearpaw Sea, last of the western oceans, reached up from the south to submerge the prairies.

*Plate LXV.*

93

# The Cenozoic Era

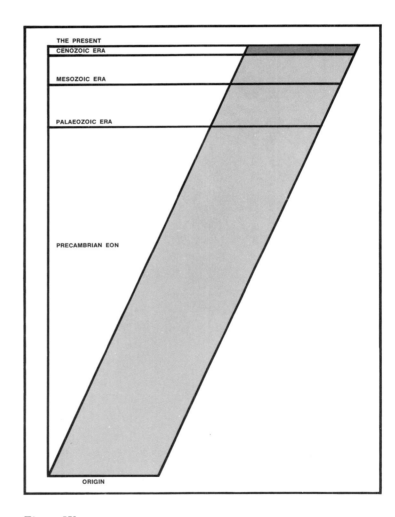

THE PRESENT
CENOZOIC ERA
MESOZOIC ERA
PALAEOZOIC ERA
PRECAMBRIAN EON
ORIGIN

*Figure IX*

# THE CENOZOIC

By the Late Cretaceous, just before the Cenozoic Era began, part of the old region we have known as 'Appalachia,' had disappeared beneath the Atlantic. The remainder of its land mass, extending north to Newfoundland, now took its configuration and has changed little during the entire Cenozoic. The Appalachian Mountains of to-day might more accurately be termed 'hills'; but they have withstood the elements for three hundred million years, and exist as the most ancient ranges of the United States, and still the primary mountain system of Eastern North America.

They include the Notre Dame Mountains of Quebec on the Gaspé Peninsula, to stretch southwest for fifteen hundred miles, forming a divide between the rivers meeting the Atlantic and those that drain into the Gulf of Mexico. South of our borders the Adirondacks, Alleghenys, Blue Ridge Mountains, Great Smokies and Catskills all are remnants of the giant crags of Appalachia that reared skyward in the Pennsylvanian.

In the Early Cenozoic came the 'Laramide Revolution' which formed the Eastern Cordillera,—the Canadian Rockies. Tremendous disturbances must have been felt all over Earth; crustal heaving of unbelievable proportions forced upward the materials which had gathered in the Cordilleran trough for more than a billion years, to culminate in the tortured twisting of rock masses that are now the most beautiful and rugged scenery on this continent.

Directly after the Laramide or Rocky Mountain orogeny, or perhaps partially synonymous with it came renewed mountain-building in the *Western*

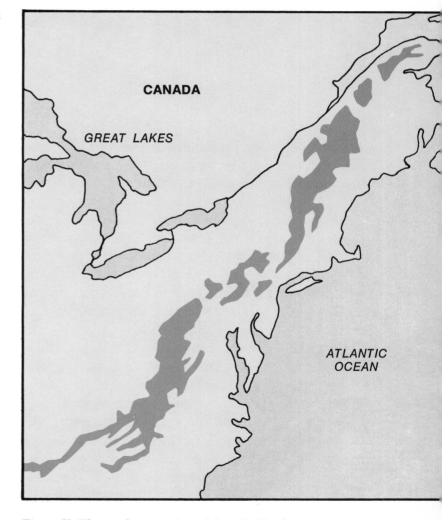

*Figure X. The northern portion of* Appalachia *that still exists to-day.*

Cordillera; the interior ranges of British Columbia, worn almost flat by erosion, were again uplifted by turbulence that carried through the Cenozoic and may still be in process even now.

Vulcanism, too, continued through much of the era, most pronounced in the West. Heavy lava deposits in the United States extend northward into Southern British Columbia, and the rolling hills of the Kamloops and Cache Creek country have been carved from an upper strata composed almost entirely of Tertiary lava flows.

Life as we know it began to take shape. With their huge enemies gone, the mammals made rapid gains, and Science still searches for the secret of the Mesozoic extinction that created their opportunity. Among the many theories regarded as possible, perhaps the most intriguing, (if not the most likely,) is that the insectivores, little rat-like creatures who were the earliest mammal ancestors of Man, developed a liking for reptile eggs. It would not be the only time in history that a small, timid quarry has inadvertently or instinctively found a way to defeat a giant adversary.

'Tertiary' and 'Quaternary,' the two periods of the Cenozoic, are misleading or redundant names as applied to the time sequences they represent. But, since it is our purpose to follow the events that built Canada, and not to dispute geologic terminology, their lack of descriptive meaning is of little importance:

The Tertiary is divided into five epochs before the time of glaciation, designated by the names Paleocene, Eocene, Oligocene, Miocene and Pliocene. The Quaternary includes the Pleistocene, (the great ice age,) and Holocene or Recent Time, (postglacial to the present.)

# THE TERTIARY PERIOD
67,000,000 to 5,000,000 B P

*Events of the Tertiary completed Canada's terminal stages of land formation, and defined most of our geographic features as they appear on present-day maps. The general unrest and mountain-building of the time doubtless created changes in ocean and air movements, and had a great deal to do with the origin of the world glaciation which would follow. Throughout most of the Tertiary, climates were temperate, as evidenced by the luxuriant plant life. There were hardwood forests in Greenland and Siberia; figs and magnolias grew in Alaska, suggesting an environment there much like that of Florida to-day. Near the end of the period the warm-weather plants and animals migrated southward, as the air grew progressively cooler toward the advance of the Ice Ages.*

The great plains continued to rise, their uplift increasing toward the West. Further thrust-faulting was sustained in the young Canadian Rockies; early in the period their construction was complete, and Eocene time saw rivers flowing eastward from the newly-formed mountains, carrying their loads of sediments to blanket the lower land.

Half the rivers in Canada are fed by waters from melting ice in the Rockies. From the glacier that bears its name, the great Athabasca wends its way to the Arctic; through the valleys of the Bow, the Red Deer, and the North and South Saskatchewan the meltwaters travel more than a thousand miles to empty into Lake Winnipeg, before resuming their journey to Hudson's Bay via the Nelson. And from the Continental Divide the Thompson, the Columbia and the mighty Fraser flow west to reach the Pacific.

The influence that the Rockies exert on weather conditions has been constant since their formation; more than fifty million years before ever Man saw the light of day, the distinctive Chinook cloud arched across the mountains, and the warm alpine winds that are the present-day phenomena of Southern Alberta, raised the temperatures of western winters as much as seventy degrees in a few hours.

The enormous Alberta coal deposits can be dated to the early Tertiary as well as to the preceding period, suggesting heavy growths of swamps and vegetation after the Cretaceous seas withdrew. As the last of these oceans receded, probably over the space of several million years, almost all of the present land mass was left exposed. Hudson's Bay did not yet exist. Canada's coastlines still extended much farther than they do to-day, the Pacific coast lying miles west of Vancouver Island. The Atlantic margin subsided a little, admitting the sea westward, and Appalachia lifted gently.

Late in the period the seas encroached still farther on the west coast, pushing the shoreline inland. The coastal islands off British Columbia, merely higher land points in the previous mainland, were now isolated and surrounded by water.

Possibly a rise in the ocean levels, and not down-warping of land, was the cause of the changes at this time; the eastern coastline was also forced back as the Atlantic took more territory. Appalachia became slightly more elevated, and the gulf and valley of the St. Lawrence took shape, though there is still no evidence of the Great Lakes basins.

The plant life was not unlike that of the present, excepting perhaps in distribution. Grasses and hardwoods in particular were quite 'modern.' In Early

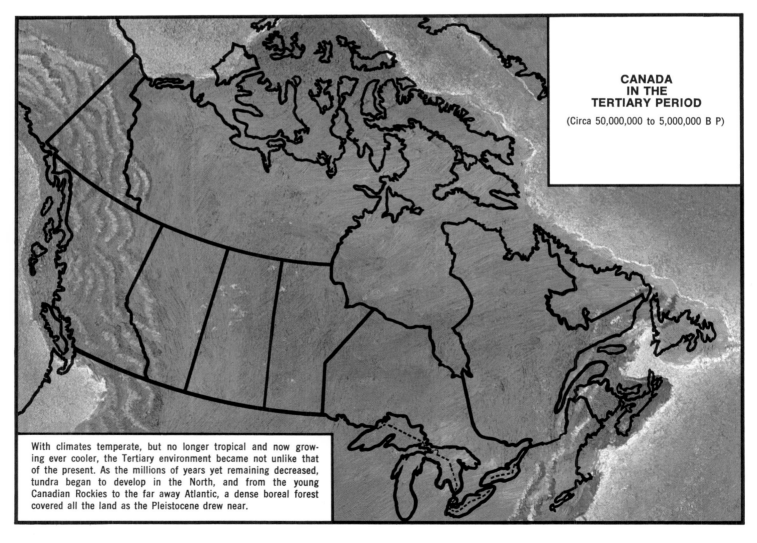

**CANADA
IN THE
TERTIARY PERIOD**

(Circa 50,000,000 to 5,000,000 B P)

With climates temperate, but no longer tropical and now growing ever cooler, the Tertiary environment became not unlike that of the present. As the millions of years yet remaining decreased, tundra began to develop in the North, and from the young Canadian Rockies to the far away Atlantic, a dense boreal forest covered all the land as the Pleistocene drew near.

*Plate LXVI.*

Tertiary the mountain country of the North was covered by evergreens, while subtropical growth still flourished in the lowlands. Deciduous forest stretched across the coastal plains and continental interior. By Late Miocene the coniferous stands of spruce and pine had spread to most of Canada, and before the Ice Age rich boreal forest extended from Alaska to Oregon, and across the North and East to the Atlantic.

Mammal life reigned supreme, and almost all species developed in size and population. Modern birds had replaced the first 'toothed' varieties of the Mesozoic.

Before the end of the Miocene a drop of some fifteen degrees in average temperatures, appears to have taken place over a time span of about four million years. Further decreases continued throughout the eight million years of the Pliocene. Less than *half* of the Late Tertiary cooling, would have been more than adequate to trigger the chain-reaction growth of the Pleistocene glaciers.

*Plate LXVII. Early carnivores.*

# THE FIVE EPOCHS OF
# THE TERTIARY

67,000,000 to 57,000,000 B P

## 1. The Palaeocene

The ten million year duration of the Palaeocene Epoch appears to have been a time of quiet, and gathering preparation for the surge of mammal growth and mountain-making which was to follow in the Eocene. The only marine deposits of any note in Canada are on the central plains, where there was some deposition as the Cretaceous seas withdrew.

Temperate to subtropical climate conditions prevailed, and familiar hardwoods such as oak and hickory grew in the widespread deciduous forests.

None of the large mammals had yet appeared. The insectivore group included little creatures much like rats and opossums, and among the primates were tarsiers and lemurs. Birds had 'modernised;' their teeth had disappeared and reptilian skins or scales had long been replaced by feathers.

The small monkey-like primates had sprung from the insectivore family. In other parts of the world their development continued toward humanoid forms, but in Canada they became extinct after the Palaeocene. No record is found of them in later times until Man, fully evolved to 'species Homo Sapiens,' returned from Asia almost sixty million years later.

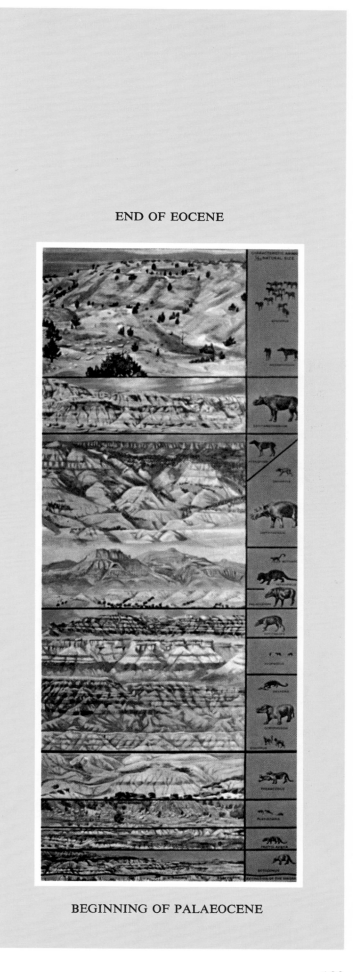

BEGINNING OF PALAEOCENE

*Plate LXVIII.*

103

*Palaeocene landscape and Life restorations.*

*Plate LXIX.*

*Plate LXX.*

*Eocene landscape and Life restorations.*

*Plate LXXI.*

*Plate LXXII.*

57,000,000 to 40,000,000 B P

## 2. The Eocene

The Tertiary's most pronounced growth and diversi-
fication of mammals, and the completion of the Canadian Rockies are the two 'spectaculars' of Eocene
time. The seventeen million years of the epoch were
turbulent in the West where the great new mountains
rose, and most of Canada was characterised by subtropical forests and little or no frost.

Large animals now populated the western plains
of North America; rhinoceros and the huge hippo-
like vegetarians became numerous as food grasses
increased. More widespread were the smaller animal
groups: true rodents had appeared, rabbits, rats and
mice. The first hoofed animal was 'Eohippus,' a tiny
horse no more than a foot tall. And Nature's newcomers now included bats, wolves and small preda-
tory cats with fangs that made them a living minia-
ture prediction of the great sabre-tooth.

The several plant-eating ungulates that resembled
overgrown editions of to-day's hippopotamus, lasted
some twenty million years. From small beginnings
they became monsters standing eight feet at the
shoulder, and all were equipped with some form of
frontal defence; the six-horned Uintatherium, the
battering-ram Titanothere, and the giant Brontother-
ium or 'thunderbeast,' carried formidable weapons
that were totally contradictory to both their peace-
loving nature and the absence of large carnivores.
Their armaments may have developed as a result of
digging, forcing paths through massed vegetation, or
could have been Nature's way of 'anticipating' the
growth of the hunting canines.

The fossils of the earliest rhinos are found by
thousands in Wyoming. Small and highly vulnerable
to predators, they spent most of their lives in streams
or shallow water. They were a wandering breed, and
roamed north to Canada as they reached their present size; then, from the Yukon and Alaska, they
later crossed the Bering land bridge to Asia. The
rhinoceros, like the horse and llama, originated here
and emigrated from North America, not to it.

There were few if any true extinctions in the Eocene. The predators were small and the food plentiful. There was little to interrupt the rapid progress of
the large mammals, though many species changed
sharply and are found with new names as the next
epoch begins.

*Plate LXXIII. Eocene carnivores.*

*Plate LXXIV.* Uintatherium *vegetarians.*

40,000,000 to 27,000,000 B P

## 3. The Oligocene

The little primates that lived in Canada had disappeared after the end of the Palaeocene. But now, elsewhere on Earth, vital developments were taking place in the descendants of that group. The division of lines becomes clear, trending to monkeys on the one side, and great apes, sub-man and Man on the other. No one knows in what part of the world the distinction first occurred, but fossils found in Egypt seem nearest to the dividing point.

In North America the primitive mammals began to die out, to be replaced by many of the general, if not identical types of to-day. The hippo and rhinoceros-like vegetarians still browsed the plains and swamplands. Dogs and camels had made their appearance, and rodents, sheep and small cats became almost 'modern.' There were 'cattle,' and hogs of a sort,—great, fierce tuskers that inhabited the swamps and forests. Horses had reached a height of twenty-four to thirty inches. And, (though much smaller than their successors,) the first distinct ancestors are found of the dire wolf and *Smilodon,* the famous sabre-tooth tiger of the Pleistocene.

As the thirteen million years of the epoch passed Canada's climates grew cooler, though still temperate. The subtropical forests died out, and grasses and conifers began to cover larger areas of the country.

END OF EPOCH

BEGINNING OF EPOCH

*Plate LXXV.*

*Oligocene Life and landscape restorations.*

*Plate LXXVI.*

*Plate LXXVII.*

*Plate LXXVIII.*

27,000,000 to 13,000,000 B P

## 4. The Miocene

The Life of the Miocene was again considerably advanced over that of the previous epoch. The weather still was temperate though cooling gradually, and as grasses increased, so did the rapid rise of the grazing mammals.

All of the large Oligocene plant-eaters were still present, and most of the small animals had come through as well, in somewhat larger editions. A predator vaguely like to-day's wolverine, and a hoofed creature resembling both the camel and giraffe, had appeared. Horses became pony-size and the formidable wild hog was outweighed only by the rhinoceros and his kin.

The first mastodons now came to Canada. They crossed the land bridge to Alaska, then wandered south and east. The earliest of them were not large; the familiar 'museum-size' specimens we know, are from millions of years later in the Pleistocene.

The Miocene epoch lasted fourteen million years. At least once during that time, the land bridge existed and migration took place in both directions, mingling the Life of two continents.

Across the Atlantic, the primates in Africa now left evidence of another startling development. One of their lines had branched to three distinct divisions: the great apes, which still exist; sub-man, who died out later with the extinction of the Neanderthals, and primitive Man, who began a bilateral evolution with competitors no more sub-human than himself.

*Plate LXXIX.*

END OF EPOCH

BEGINNING OF EPOCH

*Plate LXXX.*                    *Life and landscape restorations of the Miocene.*

*Plate LXXXI. Miocene horse* Hyohippus.

112

13,000,000 to 5,000,000 B P

## 5. The Pliocene

Throughout most of the Pliocene, there is evidence of free migration of animals across an almost constant Bering Land Bridge. Numerous creatures that had not evolved in North America now added their number to the fast-multiplying indigenous breeds, and the land literally swarmed with life.

Among the newcomers were bears, moose and mammoths, foxes and ground squirrels, the strange glyptodons from the south and the giant sloths. Mastodons, horses and the sabre-tooth cats had all doubled their size.

As the temperatures dropped the tall lush grasses gave way to shorter varieties, but still the mammals grew larger with every passing century. Both plant and animal life were now almost totally 'modernised;' eighty percent of the Pliocene species still exist to-day.

The eight million years of the epoch were the last phase of Tertiary Time. The air grew ever cooler, and all Life developed protective garments and began to move slowly southward as the great Ice Age drew near.

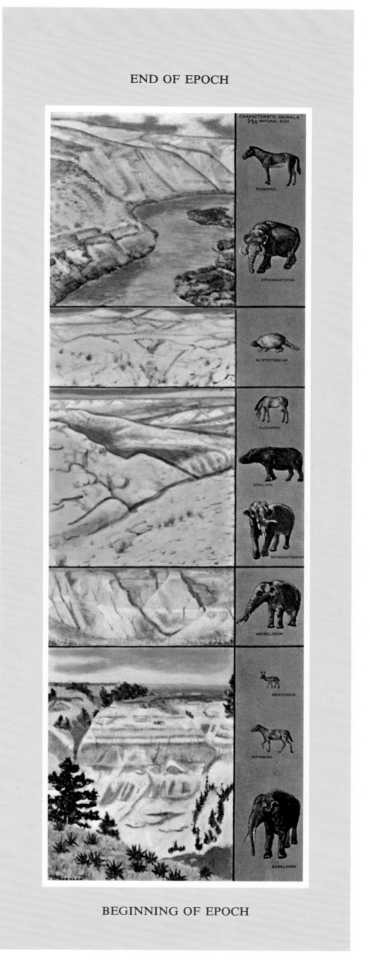

BEGINNING OF EPOCH

*Plate LXXXII.*

113

*Pliocene Life and landscape restorations.*

*Plate LXXXIII.  Giant Sloths.*

114

*Plate LXXXIV. Pliocene horse (Pliohippus.).*

# The Quaternary Period

**Table I: The Quaternary Period*** 

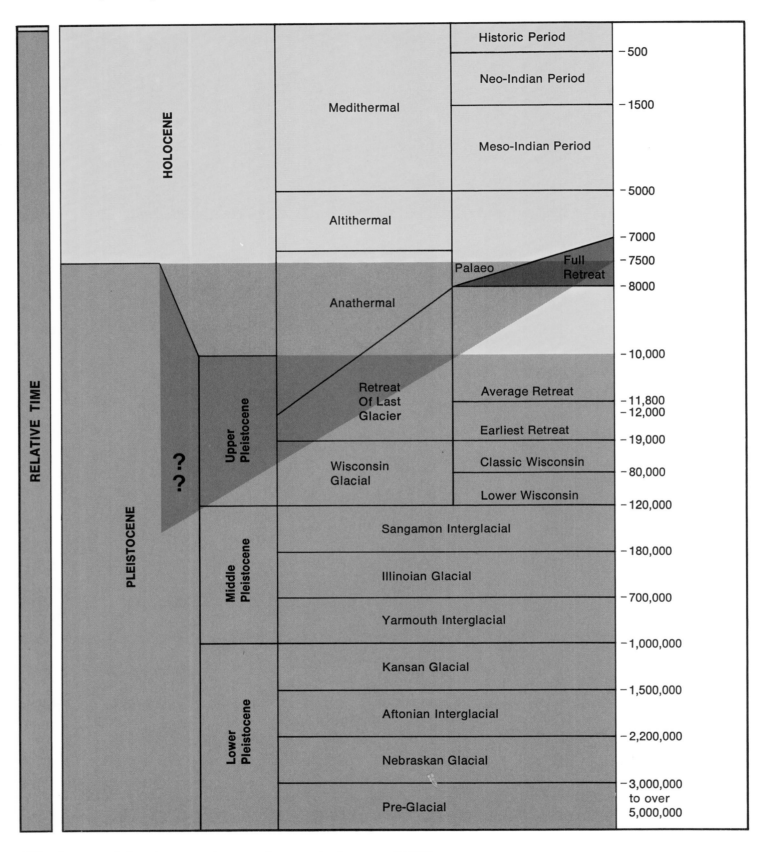

| | | | | |
|---|---|---|---|---|
| | | | Historic Period | −500 |
| | | Medithermal | Neo-Indian Period | −1500 |
| | HOLOCENE | | Meso-Indian Period | |
| | | Altithermal | | −5000 |
| | | | | −7000 |
| | | | Palaeo / Full Retreat | −7500 |
| | | Anathermal | | −8000 |
| | | | | −10,000 |
| | Upper Pleistocene | Retreat Of Last Glacier | Average Retreat | −11,800 / −12,000 |
| | | | Earliest Retreat | −19,000 |
| | | Wisconsin Glacial | Classic Wisconsin | −80,000 |
| | | | Lower Wisconsin | −120,000 |
| | Middle Pleistocene | Sangamon Interglacial | | −180,000 |
| PLEISTOCENE | | Illinoian Glacial | | −700,000 |
| | | Yarmouth Interglacial | | −1,000,000 |
| | Lower Pleistocene | Kansan Glacial | | −1,500,000 |
| | | Aftonian Interglacial | | −2,200,000 |
| | | Nebraskan Glacial | | −3,000,000 to over 5,000,000 |
| | | Pre-Glacial | | |

RELATIVE TIME

?.?

*The duration of the Pleistocene is currently recognised at three milion years, with new findings pointing to four, five million or more. Dates shown for the glacial phases are the latest accepted figures, to the Illinoian. Most publications still give younger dates for the Sangamon and Wisconsin.*

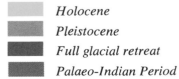

Holocene
Pleistocene
Full glacial retreat
Palaeo-Indian Period

# THE QUATERNARY
From the Pliocene to the Present

*The Quaternary is the current time period, in which we live. Sometimes called the Psychozoic, or 'Age of Man,' it is but a brief few million years in process. And at least as much is known of the history of those years, as we know of the preceeding* four billion.

The present form of Hudson's Bay took shape as the north seas reached in from the Arctic; (this predates the postglacial uplifts and probably occurred in early Pleistocene time.) The floor of the Gulf of St. Lawrence, too, is overlain by glacial materials; the Laurentian Channel is a pre-galcial trough that was modified by the ice.

The four great glaciations of the Pleistocene have come and gone, but whether or not the last recession only some ten thousand years ago was the end of the Ice Age itself, we can only guess. The climates and temperatures of the three interglacial periods were not unlike those of the present. The remnants of the great glaciers still exist, and a coincidence of climatic conditions could again set into motion their cycle of growth. We may well be living in the *fourth* interglacial interval; ten, twenty or a hundred thousand years from now, Canada could again be in the grip of the advancing ice sheets.

The pattern followed by the Ice Age maximums is one that places most of the current northern communities of the human race, directly in their path: a path where four times in the past, the viscous blankets of living ice have moved, their grinding force contemptuous of any lesser obstacle than the towering Canadian Rockies.

It may be a comforting thought that while interglacial periods have usually occupied some hundred thousand years or more, civilisations have not generally lasted over a few thousand. Or indeed that Man's technology, already advanced to some control of the elements, may in another few hundred years be capable of reversing any threatening trend of 'snowballing' precipitation.

A glacier, almost humanoid in its laws of existence, is a moving, living thing which by its own progress must destroy itself. An unusual amount of snow-producing condensation in one area begins the reaction; it then 'creates its own cold,' growing as that refrigeration forces further precipitation from the air currents that pass over it. But its optimum size is reached when it has hoarded so much moisture that no quantity still available from Earth's other reserves, is any longer sufficient to support its thirst. Then glacial decay sets in, and is uncontrollable; melting creates conditions which cause further melting, and as the ice sheet recedes so must recede its influence on the weather.

Our interpretations of the cause of the glacial periods are incomplete and hypothetical. The primary temperature drops that took place on Earth may *not* have been the *source* of the Pleistocene glaciations, but simply have made them *possible*. Science has now shown that a change of *as little as four degrees*, could again start in Canada a glacial centre and its resultant inexorable spread. The great Laurentide ice cap may have been originated by one unusual encounter of warm winds from the Pacific and a cold Arctic air mass, and the condensation they produced.

The temperature reductions *themselves* have not been explained: the changes that determined the present position of the poles and the Equator, have been suggested as a reason; or, a solar system move-

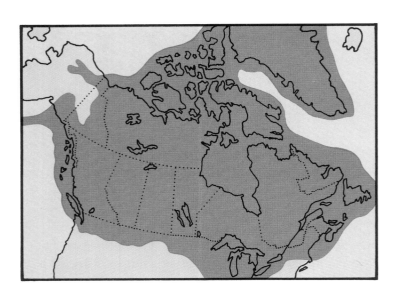

*Figure XI. Maximum cover of the Quaternary glaciations.*

ment may have taken Earth to a greater distance from the Sun. Considering the waning and recurring nature of the ice maximums, it is also possible that Earth's orbiting of the Sun may at times have been more elliptical than we now know it.

Whatever their cause, the environmental fluctuations of the Quaternary have been intense, and a host of living creatures have been replaced by forms better equipped for survival. During the Pleistocene the Isthmus of Panama lay dry as well as Bering Strait. Over these land bridges the Life of all the major continents now merged as the animals migrated. They mingled, interbred and developed,—and the strongest, most adaptable of them exist to-day. Man is among them, and we, through our European and Asian ancestors, owe much of our physical character to the rigors of the Ice Age.

Still, glaciation should be regarded as the *punctuation* of the Quaternary, not as its only important feature. The period has also, thus far, been a time of continued vulcanism, progressive continental uplift, and the final shaping of the land and coastlines as they appear to our generation. And,—above all, the coming of Man to North America.

# THE PLEISTOCENE
The Great Ice Age

*The Pleistocene was the vital 'time cradle' of the human race;—the epoch in which Man evolved from the lesser life forms that preceded him.*

*For millions of years the great ice sheets gripped the Canadian portion of North America, through four major advances and retreats. The Wisconsin alone, last and perhaps briefest of the glacial stages, may have lasted over a thousand centuries.*

## The Time of the Glaciers

In the physical history of Canada, the glaciations of the Pleistocene have been responsible for the very character of this land. Rolling moraines with their gravel and till are the stony surfaces that make up our rangelands and forests. The richest farmlands are country that was covered by glacial lakes, and their resulting deposits of fine-grained soils. Most of our rivers would be dry part of each year and raging torrents at other times but for glacial remnants that hold vast storage quantities of water, regulating runoff.

The mining industry was heavily affected, when the abrasive ice sheets stripped away the upper rock from many surface ore bodies which would otherwise have remained buried. The sands and gravels we use in construction, and also the 'gumbo' of the prairies are often glacial deposits. Most of our cities are located in valleys or lowlands of glacial drift; and the Wisconsin sculptured Canada's most scenic landscapes—lakes, hills and ridges, all modified by the movement of the ice.

Sources published very recently still stated the beginning of the Pleistocene to be one million years ago or less. Prior to 1970 new findings had pushed this date back to three million, which is still the figure most widely recognised. Now, however, there is again new evidence, and dates of four and five million years are not only being considered, but have already been accepted by some contemporary scientists. In 1971, 'positive' dates had been obtained, on areas of major glaciation which are 4,500,000 years old.

We have seen that it was possible for glacial centres to originate at any time in the Pliocene, or even earlier. There is good possibility that findings of the next few years will place the onset of the Ice Age at a much earlier date than is now believed. Bearing in mind that the length of the epoch could be as little as three million years or in excess of five, our own discussion of the Pleistocene is based on a probable duration of five million years.

121

*Plate LXXXV. A simulated landscape of the Ice Age.*

122

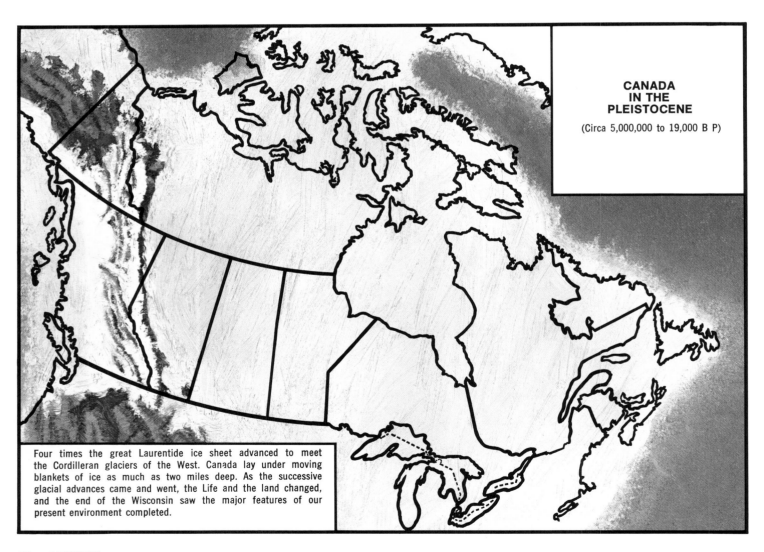

CANADA
IN THE
PLEISTOCENE

(Circa 5,000,000 to 19,000 B P)

Four times the great Laurentide ice sheet advanced to meet the Cordilleran glaciers of the West. Canada lay under moving blankets of ice as much as two miles deep. As the successive glacial advances came and went, the Life and the land changed, and the end of the Wisconsin saw the major features of our present environment completed.

Plate LXXXVI.

The four great glacial periods have been named the Nebraskan, Kansan, Illinoian and Wisconsin. The major interglacial times that separated the four phases, and during which climates were as warm as the present or more so, are called the Aftonian, Yarmouth and Sangamon. The recognised dates of their existence often change with each year of new research findings. Those shown on our Quaternary time scale are the result of the latest dating work in North America, and published opinions of the last twelve months.

The glaciers were also punctuated by interstadial periods or 'interstades,' short-term ice recessions in localised areas. The main *early* interstade in the Wisconsin occupied an estimated twenty thousand years; then a re-advance brought the Late, or 'Classic' Wisconsin period. There were other, briefer interstades, with the glacier reaching its climax of maximum ice cover in most areas, from 22,000 to 19,000 B P.*

Again there is conflicting chronology: latest ideas place the beginning of the Winsconsin at over 100,000, and as much as 130,000 B P. Most published material, conversely, still holds it at younger dates ranging near 80,000 B P, with a duration of about seventy thousand years. It may well be that this younger dating has interpreted a major interstade (which we now think did close after 80,000 B P,) to be the end of the Sangamon.

At any rate, the last glacial fronts were still *advancing* across the country less than twenty-five thousand years ago. During the Wisconsin the great Laurentide ice sheet, beginning in the mountains of Labrador, had reached south and west to cover Canada to the Rockies. The Cordilleran valley glaciers spread in the mountains of the West to blanket British Columbia and parts of Alaska. The Pacific Coast, fully glaciated, lay two hundred miles farther out to sea than at present, and the west coast islands were buried under ice. Much of Alaska and the Yukon escaped glaciation entirely, as did small areas in southern Alberta and Saskatchewan, and at times a corridor parallelling the eastern flanks of the Rockies. Wisconsin ice at its maximum reached depths of more than two miles in places, stretching to a point south of St. Louis.

*B P: Before Present, referring always to years before 1950.

## Life of the Pleistocene

The animals and plants of the Ice Age remained fairly constant until the end of the period, since most of them were not destroyed by the ice movements but rather displaced, to return with the interglacials. The successive waves of glaciation four times drove south all living things in their path; but the fossil record shows that many creatures stayed near the southern margin of the ice, and with each withdrawal returned to re-inhabit their northern home.

With North and South America now joined at the Panama zone after sixty-two million years of separation,—horses, camels, deer, bear, cats, dogs and mastodons spread south. Armadillos, glyptodons, raccoons, porcupines, and sloths wandered northward. On the Bering Strait Plain also, the movement was constant in both directions; among other species deer, modern bear, beaver, reindeer and caribou came to North America, while cows, horses, antelope and camels moved to Europe and Asia.

Most Canadian mammals are of Asiatic origin, but the Pleistocene migrants ranged freely between the two continents at all times that the land bridge stood above water. Those that inhabited Canada, (to name only better known species,) were:

**Table II**

| | | |
|---|---|---|
| beaver | large cats | caribou |
| muskrat | mastodon | bison |
| lemming | mammoth | yak |
| hunting dog | antelope | camel |
| wolf | elk | steppe antelope |
| giant elk | fox | moose |
| muskox | mountain sheep | horse |
| walrus | goose | tapir |
| condor | forest bison | snow sheep |
| brown bear | ermine | turkey |
| vulture | weasel | eagle |
| wolverine | lynx | hare |
| grizzly | mountain goat | black bear |
| badger | skunk | turtle |
| gopher | rat | coyote |
| bobcat | ground squirrel | giant sloth |
| deer | giant beaver | reindeer |
| sabre-tooth cats | llama | peccary |
| | | (early pig) |
| otter | mouse | quail |

The rhinoceros had died out in North America at the end of the Pliocene. Camels were extinct about ten thousand years ago.

*Panthera atrox,* the Alaskan cave lion, became extinct near the close of the Wisconsin. Carbon dates prove that he was contemporaneous with Man, as was the dire wolf. *Atrox* was a true lion in every sense, some hundred pounds heavier than the present species and otherwise almost indentical. He was a plains hunter, following the buffalo herds, and his remains are found from Alaska and the Yukon, to California.

Giant ground sloths that stood twenty feet tall browsed on the branches of shrubs and small trees. Slow and docile by nature, they were ready prey for large cats and later for Man, in spite of a kind of armour formed by bone growths in their outer skin.

Glyptodons shared most of the same times and areas that were inhabited by the sloths. Shell-covered and spike-tailed, they were ancestors of to-day's armadillo, but in the Pleistocene grew to lengths of fifteen feet.

The mammoth and mastodon represented the elephant family during the Ice Age, though there never was a true *elephant* native to North America. The mammoth was a plains grazer, and the mastodon essentially a forest browser. Mastodons may have been present on the prairies, but were more common to wooded areas, (in Canada largely the North and the East.) Mammoths had developed over four million years ago, though they reached their great size in the Late Pleistocene. Mastodons are of a different genus, and had a history millions of years longer.

Both animals carried back-humps of stored fat on which they could live when forage was scarce. Both also were in contact with Man, and were hunted by him for food.

Mammoth finds with tusks up to twelve feet in length are not uncommon. The *Imperial Mammoth* was the largest, standing as high as fifteen feet at the shoulder; he had little or no hair, and ranged mostly in the warm, forested zones of the southern United States and Mexico. The *Columbian Mammoth,* somewhat more hardy, flourished in the temperate regions. *Wooly Mammoths* and mastodons had long, shaggy hair underlain by fur, and frequented the northern areas of Canada and the Arctic.

Horses, evolving through smaller forms during Tertiary Time, had now reached their modern size and were also part of early Man's diet. Though they had migrated from here to Asia and lived on, for some reason they became extinct in North America about 10,000 BP. They were re-introduced by Europeans in the year 1519, and did not reappear in Canada until some four hundred years ago.

The origin of some species seems indeterminate. The squirrel, for example, could not easily have migrated from anywhere;—being a small forest animal, the plains or steppes would have been an insurmountable barrier to him.

The largest Ice Age carnivore was the short-faced bear, in bulk about equal to the present Kodiak.

Sabre-tooth cats were all extinct before the accepted time of human migration, and it is unlikely that Man ever saw a *Smilodon* in Canada. The great sabre-tooth of the Pleistocene was the culmination of

*Plate LXXXVII. Wooly Rhinoceros of the earliest glacial period.*

*Plate LXXXVIII. Northern Mammoth and Mastodon.*

128

*Plate LXXXIX*. Smilodon, *the sabre-tooth tiger*.

*Plate XC. Irish Elk of the Pleistocene. (Eastern Canada)*

*Plate XCI. Giant Bison of the Ice Age.*

130

his breed. Other cats of the Cenozoic were evolving in patterns that would escape extinction to become the feline groups of to-day, including our small domestic variety. But *Smilodon,* from all available evidence, was anything but a 'pussycat.' The small brain and weak hind quarters, the massive and powerful neck and forearms and the nine inch dagger-like upper fangs all present the picture of an insatiable killer who destroyed much more than he needed. His teeth and structure indicate that he lived chiefly on blood.

The sabre-tooth was capable of scant groundspeed at best; he probably killed by leaping from ambush to strike down with his fangs, then using them to hold the prey as on a hook, while clawing it to death. But the fossil and bone findings show also that he had hunting companions;—skulls of the ferocious dire wolves are almost always found with his remains. This suggests that the great cat did the killing and the wolves lived on the carcasses. Their minute brain cavities support the theory that they did not possess enough intelligence to subsist alone as hunters, and followed the tiger as scavengers. The coincidence of skelton remains might be explained as incidents when hunger and stupidity caused the wolf pack to rush upon the kill before the cat had left it.

The buffalo arrived in two main waves of migration, in the Illinoian and Wisconsin. They spread rapidly and soon populated the plains and tundra in vast numbers, originating the mighty herds of early Canadian history.

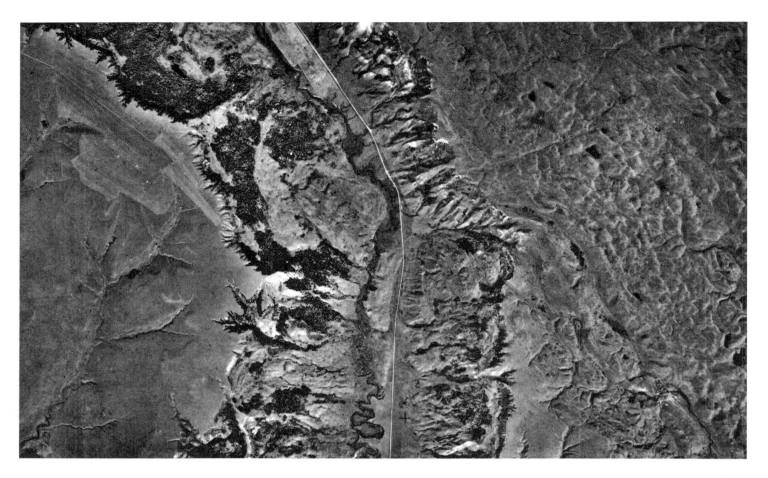

Figure XII. The Cypress Hills of Saskatchewan
escaped glaciation. The western end moraine of the
Laurentide Glacier, and the meltwater channel,
are shown above.

Plate XCII. "The Erratics," quartzite blocks at Okotoks,
which were displaced by ice movements.

## The Classic Wisconsin

Continental uplift continued throughout most of the Pleistocene; but in localised areas such as the Hudson's Bay Lowlands, the Great Lakes Country and others, the land remained heavily depressed by the weight of the ice sheets. The 'springback' that occurred after glacial withdrawal is still taking place. Many major features of Canada, too, were modified by the *movement* of the ice, which rounded out topographical structures such as the Okanagan Valley and a multitude of glacial lake basins.

The Okanagan formed prior to the last glaciation. Then, Cordilleran ice some sixty-three hundred feet thick lay in the valley for thousands of years, leaving glacial Lake Penticton and several smaller lakes. They remained after the ice withdrew, to originate the jewel-like reservoirs that are there to-day.

Apart from the large ice-free areas of Alaska and the Yukon, and the strip along the mountains, the only notable places in the West to escape glaciation were the Porcupine Hills of Alberta and the Cypress Hills of Southwestern Saskatchewan. The latter were bounded on the east by the end moraine of the Laurentide glacier, and by a meltwater channel some seven hundred feet deep, which drained north and east into Hudson's Bay.

The western plains and Northwest Territories were dotted with glacial lakes during interglacial periods and just after the last ice recession. Glacial Lake Regina drained south into the Mississippi system, and later as the ice pulled back farther, into Lake Agassiz, via the Qu'Appelle River Valley.

Glacial Lake Edmonton occupied the North Saskatchewan River Valley near the present city, and at one stage extended into the valley of the Athabasca.

The famous quartzite blocks at Okotoks, Alberta resulted from a meeting of the Cordilleran and Laurentide ice at one time; they are parts of a single great block of over eighteen thousand tons, which was carried by the merging ice that flowed south from its coalition point.

Lake Rycroft drained into the Peace River Valley, twelve thousand years ago. Lake Saskatchewan occupied the middle course of the present Saskatchewan River. Lake Souris in Western Manitoba drained to the valley of the James River, and Lake Wollaston discharged west to the Athabaska.

The last known of the larger glacial lakes in the west was Lake Agassiz; Lakes Winnipeg and Winnipegosis are now remnants of this giant, which emptied out into Hudson's Bay some seventy-five hundred years ago. Glacial Lake Calgary existed about 19,000 to 15,000 B P, after the last westward advance of Laurentide ice.

To carry further the chronology of the Late Wisconsin, there were partial ice recessions at about 39,000 B P, a re-advance at 25,000 with maximum cover from 22,000 to 19,000, after which the last retreat began. The interstadial periods in many localities were long enough in duration to permit the growth of forests and the extended return of animal life.

The best known non-glacial deposits of Pleistocene age in Canada, are those in Toronto's Don Valley. They have been under study for over a hundred years, and the city's recent subway excavations have brought to light a great deal of new material. Evidence is found of ancient hardwood forests, and only a little imagination is needed to picture the great stands of oak and maple on the riverside, the deer, bear and buffalo that came to drink, and the work of the giant beaver.

In the valley of the St. Lawrence were forests of sugar maples, yellow birch and balsam poplar. From interstades in Newfoundland are found ferns, sedges, orchids, willows, berries and the fossils of bear, wolf and caribou. The remains of large grazing animals are found in Labrador and the Hudson's Bay region. In the Arctic grew tundra vegetation much as it is to-day, except for birch and alder that were there in the Pleistocene.

Vancouver Island and the Vancouver city area were unglaciated at 24-25,000 BP for a time, but on the island there is also evidence of forests almost forty thousand years ago.

On the plains, as glaciation receded eastward a shrubby tundra developed, then forests of spruce, poplar and willow where only prairie exists now. This took place first in Alberta some seventeen thousand years ago; about 14,000 the terrain had changed to grasslands, which by 10-12,000 B P had reached into Saskatchewan and then Manitoba.

Radiocarbon dates recorded in the last few years by the Geological Survey of Canada provide a picture of areas that were intermittently ice-free, during Late Pleistocene interstades:

### Table III

| DATED MATERIAL | AREA | APPROXIMATE AGE (YEARS BEFORE PRESENT) |
| --- | --- | --- |
| Forest samples | Woodbridge, Ont. | 50,000 |
| Forest samples | Port Talbot, Ont. | 50,000 |
| Forest samples | Riding Mountain, Man. | 30,000 |
| Forest samples | Bruce Mountain, Baffin | 39,600 |
| Forest samples | Medicine Hat, Alta. | 24,000 |
| Willow | Banks Island | 40,600 and 49,000 |
| Spruce | Oldman River, Alta. | 54,500 |
| Sedge | Ellesmere Island | 41,200 |
| Forest | Shuswap (B.C.) | 20,000 |
| Freshwater Shells | Merritt, B.C. | 37,200 |
| Wood | Snake River, Yukon | 31,000 |
| Wood | Porcupine River, Yukon | 41,300 |
| Wood | Northwest Territory | 38,300 |
| Freshwater Shells | Kamloops, B.C. | 24,000 |
| Wood | Cape Breton | 51,000 |
| Wood | Cape Breton | 44,000 and 38,300 |
| Peat | Scarborough, Ont. | 40,000 |
| Plants and grass | Duck Mountain, Man. | 37,700 |
| Plants and grass | Minnedosa, Man. | 31,300 |
| Wood | Kamloops, B.C. | 32,700 |
| Wood | Vancouver, B.C. | 40,000 |
| Wood | Yukon | 40,100 |
| Wood | Yukon | 46,500 |
| Wood | King Point, Yukon | 51,100 |
| Peat | Northwest Territory (Eskimo Lakes) | 50,900 |
| Wood | Little Abitibi River, Ont. | 43,600 |
| Wood | Lanigan, Sask. | 42,100 |
| Plants | Medicine Hat, Alta. | 28,000 and 46,700 |
| Wood | Lynn Valley (N. Vancouver) | 52,300 |
| Wood | Shellmouth, Man. | 41,000 |
| Peat | Spring Valley, Sask. | 38,000 |
| Wood | Taber, Alta. | 35,000 |

## The End of the Wisconsin

*The growth or withdrawal of a major ice sheet occupies ten thousand years or more. While some areas were deglaciated much earlier, the retreat of the last glaciation averages 11,800 B P, with full recession to present levels, by approximately 7,000.*

About nineteen thousand years ago the climates of Earth began a steady warming trend, as they had done in the Aftonian, Yarmouth and Sangamon. Over the next hundred centuries or so, the temperatures in Canada gradually increased. The mighty Laurentide and Cordilleran glaciers gave ground and their hoard of water was released, first to the great glacial lakes, then to the oceans as the resilient land slowly recovered.

By 17,000 B P the ice front was roughly two hundred miles south of Lake Michigan, and at about 15,000 had begun to uncover the southern lobes of the Great Lakes. The St. Lawrence Valley, Maritimes and Newfoundland were largely clear before 13,000, the North Bay and Lakehead areas by about 12,000. Most of the southern plains was deglaciated by 14-15,000 B P, and the Calgary foothills may well have been ice-free as much as twenty-five thousand years ago.

The last ice drew back from the coastal lands near Vancouver, and the western islands, about 11-12,000 B P. Northern areas of Quebec, Ontario and the central plains remained glaciated until seven to nine thousand years ago.

## The Pleistocene Extinctions

Toward the end of the Pleistocene many animal species became extinct in North America, coinciding with recession of the ice and warming of the climate. Those that remained were drastically reduced, in size and numbers. In a brief few thousand years mammoths, mastodons, horses, camels, cave bears, sloths, dire wolves, lions, tigers and a host of lesser known mammals passed out of being;—and the reason, again, is unknown.

Twice before, a major life group had been mysteriously erased in a relatively short period: two hundred and forty million years ago at the beginning of Triassic time, countless billions of marine creatures had vanished; near the end of the Mesozoic the dinosaurs, after ruling unchallenged for more than a hundred and fifty million years, had disappeared. Adding to this the fate of the great mammals only a few thousand years ago a chilling premonition is raised, by the grim reminder that in each case their rise to supremacy appears to have triggered their extinction.

As before, many possibilities exist including climate, disease, genetic decadence, starvation and others. If one wishes to conclude that each time the cause was identical, the most logical theory might be overbalance.

It has been suggested that the warm period after the Wisconsin and the resulting change in vegetation, deprived many breeds of their main forage sources; but those changes have not been drastic ones, and numerous plant-eaters are still here. Human hunters have also been tendered as the reason. But their effect could not have been severe enough; in point, they had been living with and preying on the same animal groups for many thousands of years before, in Europe and Asia.

Whatever the cause, much of the Pleistocene fauna has disappeared forever in the endless chain of evolution, most of its remnants obliterated by the grinding glaciers. But enough evidence remains to build a picture,—the epic and environment of the first Canadian. He lived next to Nature in a savage land, contemporary with mountains of living ice, preying upon vegetarian giants, and pitting his human brain against predators that we can only attempt to reconstruct.

*Figure XIII. Stages in the recession of Wisconsin ice. Latest findings now indicate that it may be in order to increase many of the dates shown, by an additional five hundred years or more.*

136

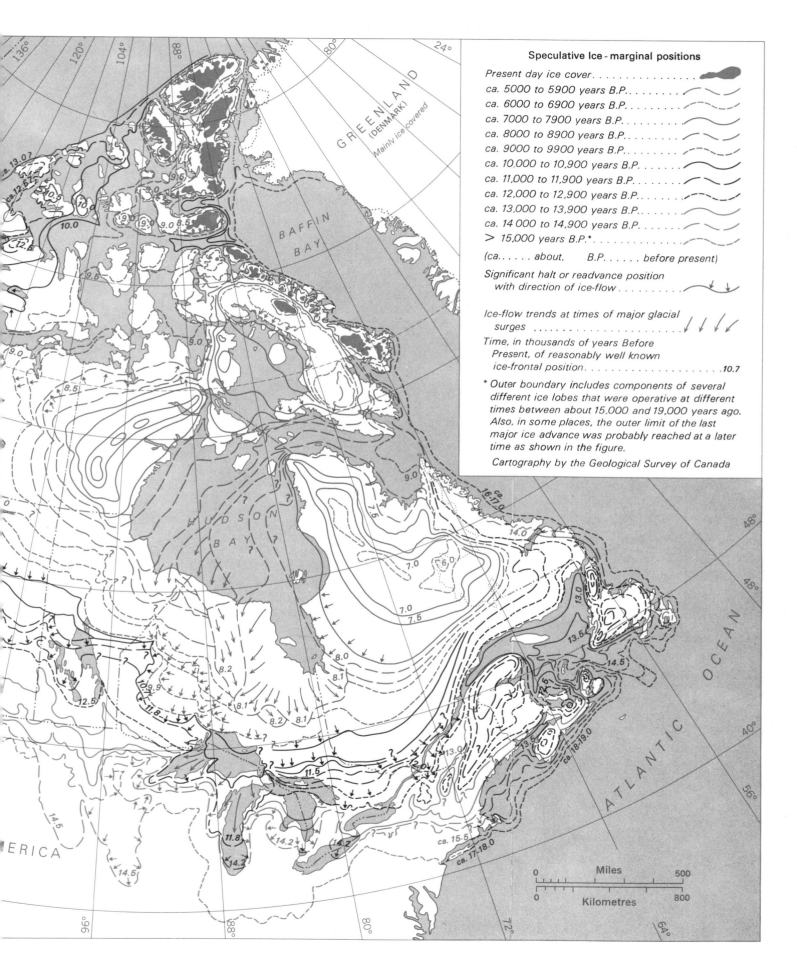

### Speculative Ice - marginal positions

Present day ice cover . . . . . . . . . . . . . . . .
ca. 5000 to 5900 years B.P. . . . . . . . .
ca. 6000 to 6900 years B.P. . . . . . . . .
ca. 7000 to 7900 years B.P. . . . . . . . .
ca. 8000 to 8900 years B.P. . . . . . . . .
ca. 9000 to 9900 years B.P. . . . . . . . .
ca. 10,000 to 10,900 years B.P. . . . . . .
ca. 11,000 to 11,900 years B.P. . . . . . .
ca. 12,000 to 12,900 years B.P. . . . . . .
ca. 13,000 to 13,900 years B.P. . . . . . .
ca. 14 000 to 14,900 years B.P. . . . . . .
> 15,000 years B.P.* . . . . . . . . . . . . .

(ca. . . . . . about,     B.P. . . . . . before present)

Significant halt or readvance position
   with direction of ice-flow . . . . . . . . . .

Ice-flow trends at times of major glacial
   surges . . . . . . . . . . . . . . . . . . . . . . .

Time, in thousands of years Before
   Present, of reasonably well known
   ice-frontal position. . . . . . . . . . . . . . . . . . . .10.7

\* Outer boundary includes components of several
   different ice lobes that were operative at different
   times between about 15,000 and 19,000 years ago.
   Also, in some places, the outer limit of the last
   major ice advance was probably reached at a later
   time as shown in the figure.

Cartography by the Geological Survey of Canada

137

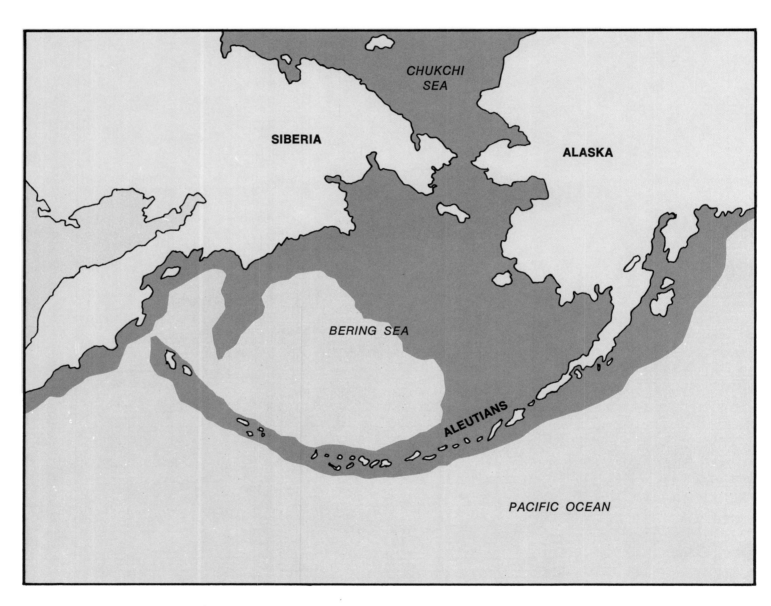

*Figure XIV. Map of 'Beringia', blue areas showing
maximum extent of the Land Bridge.*

# THE BERING LAND BRIDGE
## The Cenozoic Road to Asia

*The land bridge, even if we consider only its more recent exposures, existed for periods far greater than all the time of human occupation in North America. Across it the Life of the northern continents merged, but the creatures that migrated were not transient in any true sense;—they lived for generations on the tundra plains that joined our west coasts with Asia.*

The Anadyr-Chukotka region of Siberia, or Chukotski Peninsula, is mountainous country much like Northwestern North America. The Anadyr Range and the Brooks Range of Alaska, to-day present almost identical alpine terrains. Between them is the land of the continental plateaux, which many times became the Bering Land Bridge. The shallow waters of Bering Strait and the Bering and Chukchi Seas lie over this land formation, which separates the distinct ocean valley of the North Pacific from the basins of the Arctic and North Atlantic Oceans.

The land bridge generally stood above water at all of the peak glacial periods, when the icecaps accumulated vast stores of moisture and Earth's ocean levels were sharply reduced. If the present sea level were to drop something over one hundred feet, the bridge would again join the two continents. A drop of about three hundred feet, (less than that occurring in the Wisconsin maximums,) would create a plain some thousand miles wide from north to south.

Geology defines nine distinct intervals from the Pliocene to the present when the sea has covered Bering Strait as it does now,—(six of them during the Pleistocene.) Between these intervals the land bridge stood dry. There is also good evidence that it existed at least once in the Miocene, and throughout the majority of Pliocene Time. The earliest durations of a dry Bering Strait, (particularly those in the Neogene,*) are undateable. But the periods in the Late Pleistocene are defined with a fair degree of accuracy.

The bridge appears to have existed for a short time 10,000 to 13,000 years ago, a more extended interval 14,000 to 28,000 and a longer period ending some time over 40,000 B P, which may have origin-

*Miocene, Pliocene and Pleistocene Epochs.*

nated as far back as the end of the Sangamon, more than one hundred thousand years in the past.

Though the bridge was dry during both Illinoian and Wisconsin glaciations, the land migrations over the northerly route were probably limited to the Late Wisconsin, since at other times it could well have been totally blocked by ice. In fact, due to ice barriers and climatic conditions, there are only three logical periods when migration of land creatures was possible over the interior or northern route: the first over 40,000 years ago; the second 28,000 to 23,000, and the third 13,000 to 10,000 B P. The Illinoian and earlier glaciations were more severe than the Wisconsin, and at these times the land area that lay to the south along the Aleutians, was probably open. At the highest times of the Bering bridge the Aleutian Islands were part of it; the Alaska Peninsula was larger than at present, and terminated in what is now Umnak Island. To-day's Aleuts are probably the most direct descendants of the people who lived on 'Beringia,' as archaeologists term the area. The islands were never 'stepping stones' from Asia to North America; all migration moved by either the interior or the coastal route, on the land bridge.

The bridge itself was a broad plain, its monotony broken by numerous lakes and rivers, and a generous growth of vegetation. It had a cold, arctic type of climate, and in glacial maximums its northern reaches were intermittently covered by ice. It never supported forest, but was more a 'steppe' or low tundra region that may closely have resembled the prairies of Canada's Mid-west. While faunal migration took place in both directions, the heaviest movement was from west to east, continuing throughout the Pleistocene and earlier.

There is fairly strong evidence of at least *contact* by Man as early as 28,000 B P, and no facts that *rule out* much earlier arrivals. Pleistocene mammals grazed on the grasses of Beringia, and Man gravitated from Asia to dwell there, not exploring but simply making his home in proximity to his source of meat.

The bridge played a long and vital role in the development of to-day's North America. For millions of years the animals and plant life combined evolution and hybridisation, to produce the forms best adapted to their present ecology. Early Man, who followed his food and dispersed as naturally as he does on any liveable terrain, quite unwittingly discovered and populated a new world—without ever having been aware that he had 'migrated.'

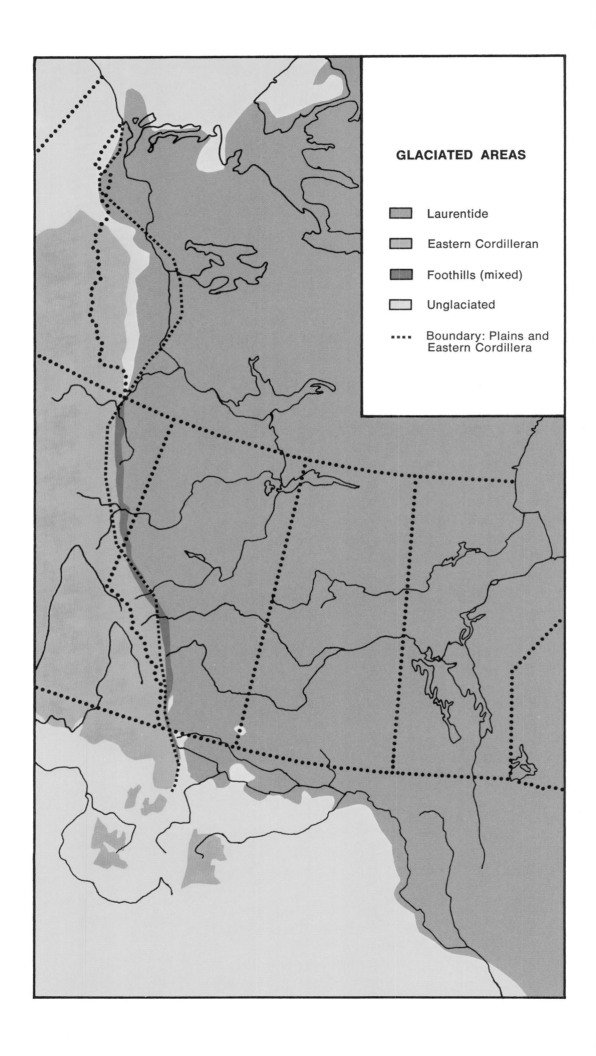

GLACIATED AREAS

Laurentide

Eastern Cordilleran

Foothills (mixed)

Unglaciated

···· Boundary: Plains and
Eastern Cordillera

# THE ROCKY MOUNTAIN CORRIDOR
The Way to the Interior

*During all the ice ages, the patterns of glaciation had left open an intermittent passage to the heart of the North American continent. Through Alaska and the Yukon, the Northwest Territory and British Columbia first the animal migrants, and now Man, found access to the valleys of the Rockies and the rolling foothills of Alberta, where shelter and game were abundant and the land lay open to the South.*

In Central Alaska lies a broad hinterland that was never covered by Pleistocene ice. Leading directly eastward from the plain where the Bering Land Bridge joined North America, it stretched more than a thousand miles, to reach deep into the Yukon and Northwest Territories,—then angling southeast along the eastern ranges of the Mackenzie Mountains and the Canadian Rockies.

Farther to the South, a passage continued on the eastern flanks of the Rockies. Through British Columbia and Alberta it followed foothills country that *was* glaciated at times, but where the Laurentide and Cordilleran glaciers rarely merged. The ice margins fluctuated; Cordilleran ice was *east* of the Rockies for a time at about Mid-Pleistocene, while at one or more intervals the Laurentide ice sheet reached *into* the mountains, penetrating as far as the Richardson and Mackenzie Ranges. But evidence now is that the two ice sheets *never* coalesced in most areas, and may possibly have *only* done so in the Athabasca Valley for a brief few thousand years.

The strip that lay between the moving perimeters of the glaciers, was the Rocky Mountain Corridor. Though its position shifted from time to time, it probably existed throughout the entire Pleistocene. Little doubt at all remains that it was clear from the time of the Wisconsin sub-retreat, some 39,000 years

*Figure XV. Ice frontal positions of the Laurentide and Cordilleran Glaciers. Their maximum areas of cover overlapped, but they rarely coalesced. An ice free corridor, varying in location, was open almost continually.*

ago. The short period of ice coalition in the Athabasca Valley is the only probable exception, taking place during the glacial readvance and maximum which began about 25,000 B P.

A huge glacial lake that lay in the Peace River Valley in the Rockies, has been dated at 11,600 B P. Radiocarbon dates that *prove* an open corridor have been obtained at Saskatchewan River Crossing and in the Bow Valley, the Kananaskis, the Calgary area, Milk River Ridge and other points on the migration route in Alberta. Near Medicine Hat there is again a suggestion of Man in the Sangamon, where stone pebble tools have been found in strata dating 100,000 to 160,000 years in age; but the dating is not positive, and the authenticity of the tools not unquestioned.

However possible, or even *probable* the southward ventures of Palaeo-Indians at earlier dates may be, it seems obvious that one large concentration of these people remained in their ice-free refuge in Alaska and the Yukon for thousands of years as the climates warmed. Their numbers multiplied,—then as the glaciers waned, many dispersed in an ever-increasing movement to the interior of the continent. And those who had earlier become isolated to the south, now began to gravitate to Canada again.

Man stayed with the game animals, pushing in the wake of their migrations; later, as the ice retreats continued he began to follow valleys eastward, and mountain passes to the west. But always his *earliest* evidences to be found in Western Canada, are in the foothills terrain of the Rocky Mountain Corridor.

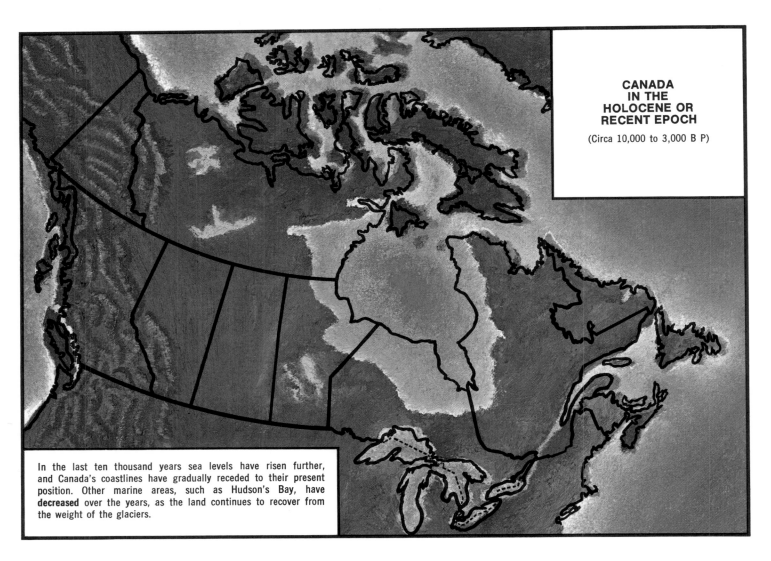

CANADA
IN THE
HOLOCENE OR
RECENT EPOCH

(Circa 10,000 to 3,000 B P)

In the last ten thousand years sea levels have risen further, and Canada's coastlines have gradually receded to their present position. Other marine areas, such as Hudson's Bay, have **decreased** over the years, as the land continues to recover from the weight of the glaciers.

*Plate XCIII.*

# THE HOLOCENE
## The Last Ten Thousand Years

*In the Holocene, or 'Recent' Epoch Canada's surface topographies have remained much as they were finished by the glaciers. There have been few alterations in structure; the expulsions of great glacial lakes and the changes in our eastern drainage systems, have been the result of* elevations—*the land's slow recovery from the depressing weight of the ice sheets.*

When Life first returned to the land after the Pleistocene, boreal forest and sub-arctic tundra were probably the most consistent scenes to be found in Canada. These surface environments moved northward as climatic changes and continued ice recession took place; in the Mid-west they were gradually replaced by the prairies and parklands that now cover the central and southern plains.

Huge forests developed in the eastern woodlands; white pines over two hundred feet tall, great oaks, maples, hickories and black walnut grew in the rich land left by the glaciers. Heavy forestation also characterised the far Southwest, where hardwoods and giant evergreens clothed the regions of the Pacific Coast.

The Canadian Shield, released from its burden of ice, now lifted progressively to the north—in a tilting fashion with hinge line south of the Great Lakes; the uplift has reached seven hundred feet at the north shore of Lake Superior, and as much as nine hundred along the eastern side of James Bay.

Vulcanism in British Columbia extended almost to the present time, and may well be experienced again. In the Spectrum Range of the Northwest are volcanic mountains which have been active as late as the last two thousand years, creating obsidian 'quarries' from which Early Man obtained material for tools. Ash fall dating about 6500 B P touches areas as far east as Saskatchewan, and appears to have originated in an unknown source in the mountains. In the Kootenay and Arrow Lakes region are ash layers no older than five hundred years, the result of atmospheric drift from volcanic action three hundred miles to the south in the United States. The only widespread volcanic strata with a *traceable* source, is the 'Bridge River' ash of Central British Columbia. About

twenty-five hundred years in age, it stems from a viscous type of eruption in which the material *flowed*

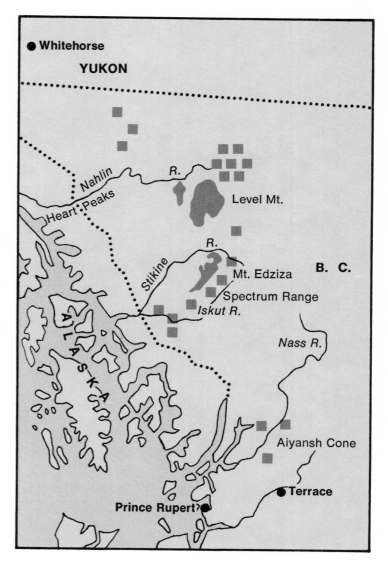

*Figure XVI. Northwestern British Columbia. The locations of Pleistocene and younger volcanoes.*

*Plate XCIV. Simulated post-glacial terrain in Early Holocene.*

from its source, rather than the commonly pictured volcanic 'explosion.'

About ninety-seven per cent of Canada's area, (more than that of any other major country on Earth,) was glaciated. Now, in the Holocene, as we search for the secrets of the past it is not surprising that there are gaps in the evidence to be found. In many of the older, deeper-lying rock stratas of the Mesozoic and Palaeozoic Eras, the evidences of Life are untouched, and are often found to be identical in both the United States and Canada. But the deposits of later time were directly exposed to the abrasive ice sheets. Some of the animals pictured in 'The Five Epochs of the Tertiary,' for example, have never been traced north of the Canadian border; but we believe that they inhabited most of North America, though their remains have been found only to the south where the record has not been further obscured by the remnants of the glaciers.

The Life of the *Holocene* on the other hand, is readily discernible from findings in Canada, many of which are still organic and have not had time to become 'fossilised.' Like the land itself, the animal types of the Epoch have remained fairly constant since the Pleistocene extinctions. Only in the latest brief period of European occupation, have numerous species again vanished, and the survival of many more become threatened.

Since the turn of this century many, like the passenger pigeon, are gone. Of the buffalo whose countless millions once blackened the plains, only a handful remain as domesticated curiosities. The wolf and

*Plate XCV. Warren Mastodon.*

*Plate XCVI. Columbia Mammoth.*

the grizzly, the marten, wolverine, mountain lion, polar bear, reindeer, caribou and eagle,—even the magnificent Canada Goose and our faunal emblem the beaver, all seem doomed to fall prey to 'civilised' Man's talent for domination of his environment,—to the eventual exclusion of all else it contains.

## Table IV

*Extinct*

| | | |
|---|---|---|
| Cormorant | Bering Island | 1852 |
| Labrador Duck | Eastern North America | 1875 |
| Heath Hen | Eastern North America | 1932 |
| Eskimo Curlew | North America | 1844 |
| Passenger Pigeon | Eastern North America | 1914 |
| Steller's sea cow | Bering Islands | 1768 |
| Sea Mink | Central East Coast | 19th century |
| 17 varieties of grizzly | North America | 19th & 20th century |
| Newfoundland wolf | Newfoundland | 20th century |
| Eastern bison | North America | 1825 |
| Oregon bison | North America | 19th century |

*Most Gravely Threatened*

| | |
|---|---|
| Whooping Crane | Mountain Lion |
| Finches | Bighorn Sheep |
| Fisher | Pronghorn Antelope |
| Beaver | Muskox |
| Marten | Bald Eagle |
| Gray Wolf | Golden Eagle |
| Grizzly | |

The secular warming trend that began with the end of Wisconsin glaciation, is still in process. It has continued throughout Recent Time, but within it three distinct and intense climatic fluctuations are recognised by Earth sciences.

A period from about twelve to seven thousand years ago, has been called the *Anathermal*. Characterised by long, severe winters, it was the time in which the maximum withdrawal of glaciers took place, and Canada was dotted by thousands of melt-water lakes.

The *Altithermal* followed, an arid period occupying some two thousand years from about 7 to 5,000 BP. The country was hot and dry in the extreme, and the western plains almost uninhabitable. Glacial lakes dried up, or were drained by the changing positions of the rising land.

The *Medithermal*, from about five thousand years ago to the present, has been a time of climates much as they are to-day. The remnants of the great glaciers

wane a little more each year; the physical uplift of many inland areas continues, and Canadians of a few thousand years from now may know a very different map of Canada.

Or, a very different map of *the world!* From our Pleistocene discussion we have seen that the Holocene may be the fourth interglacial, in which case some time in the future all Life would again be forced to the south. But a far more imminent question is posed by the *reverse* possibility: the retreat of the glaciers brought sea levels up some three hundred feet; they could be raised as much as a hundred feet *more,* if melting were to remove the remaining ice-caps in both hemispheres. Coastlines would gradually push far inland, and the sites of all the seaport cities now on Earth would be flooded by marine waters. Epeiric oceans would again lie in the interiors of continents. And Man, already crowding his terrestrial real estate, would need to discover a way to live with much less of it than he now possesses.

*Plate XCVII.* Cervalces, *early moose.*

147

## LEGEND

Recessional ice front (Laurentide); approximate, assumed . . . . . . . . .

Arrows denote a readvance, or a major halt in the recession of the ice front indicated . . . . . .

Late ice (Adirondack and Appalachian regions) . . . . . . . . . . . . . . . .

Glacial and post-glacial lakes; shore line defined or approximate, assumed . . . . . . . .

Sea; shore line defined or approximate, assumed . . . . . . . . . . . . . . .

Spillway and other lake outlet; direction lake discharge . . . . . . . . . . . .

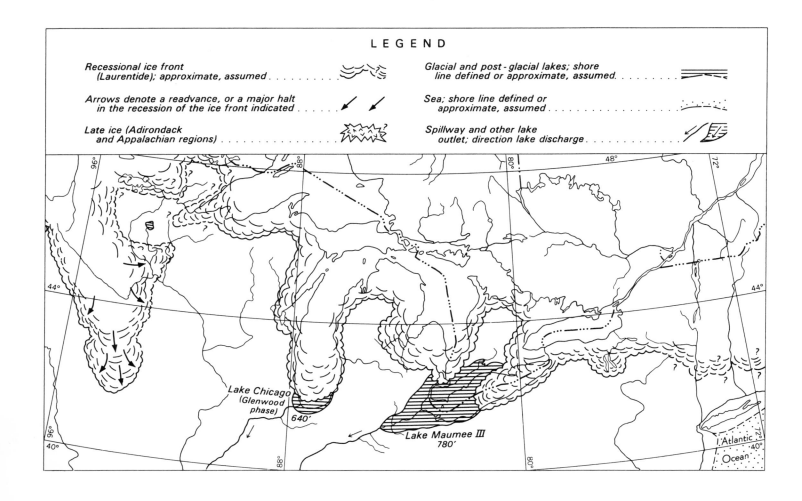

Lake Chicago (Glenwood phase)
640'

Lake Maumee III
780'

Atlantic Ocean

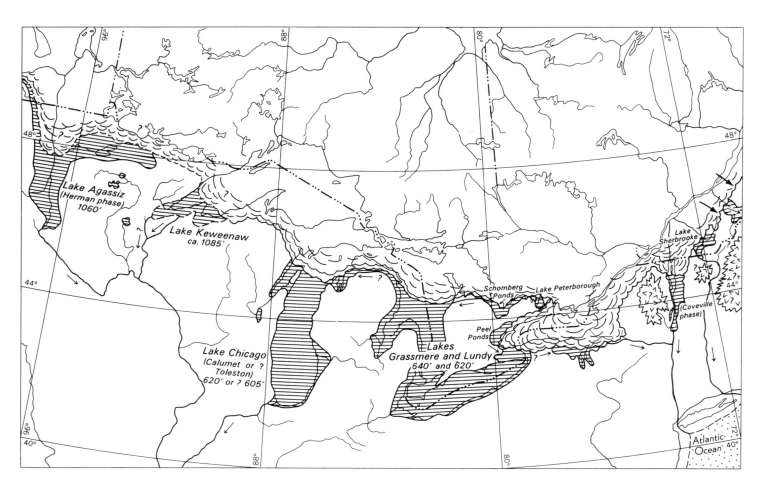

Lake Agassiz (Herman phase) 1060'

Lake Keweenaw ca. 1085'

Lake Chicago (Calumet or ? Toleston) 620' or ? 605'

Schomberg Ponds — Lake Peterborough

Peel Ponds

Lakes Grassmere and Lundy 640' and 620'

Lake Sherbrooke

(Coveville phase)

Atlantic Ocean

# NIAGARA AND THE GREAT LAKES

Legacies of the Ice Age

*As the Wisconsin Glacier receded, its meltwaters filled the basins abandoned by the moving ice, and huge glacial lakes were formed,—the forerunners of the Great Lakes of Canada. The present pattern of the lakes system was not fully established till less than three thousand years ago. Superior, to-day the largest body of fresh water on Earth, might well be termed a 'puddle' compared with such early glacial giants as its parent Lake Algonquin, or Manitoba's sprawling Lake Agassiz.*

Before the ice the Great Lakes Country was rolling land,—a fully developed part of Canada's eastern landscape. In the Tertiary Period the network of a major river system flowed eastward, into what is now the valley of the St. Lawrence.

Over millions of years the erosion of rivers and streams created a 'basin topography,'—the pattern that was to become the lake beds. As the Pleistocene glaciers advanced, the ice sheets moving into the region were guided by this pattern and further deepened the lowlands, gouging out the basins of the lakes. Each time the ice advanced, the depressions were dredged to greater depth. Huge moraine deposits left by the glaciers at their southern margins, and upheavals of the rocky terrains to the north made the 'bowls' effectively deeper.

Lake stages much like those following the Wisconsin probably existed in many interstades and interglacial periods during the entire Pleistocene, but all evidence of them has been destroyed by the most recent glaciation. The changing and complicated series of 'phases' that the lakes have undergone, has been directly or indirectly the result of the ice movements; the shifting ice fronts uncovered water outlets as they retreated, blocked existing ones as they advanced, and their melting released the discharging waters that cut new outlets. As the weight of the icecaps withdrew to the North the land lifted, to change still further the drainage complex of the waterways.

*Figure XVII.*

*Figure XVIII.*

## The Glacial Great Lakes and Niagara

From its farthest point of advance, well south of to-day's Lake Michigan, the Wisconsin Glacier began its withdrawal about 17,000 BP. Within two thousand years it had waned northward to expose the tips of Lake Chicago and Lake Maumee, which drained south through the Illinois and Wabash Rivers into the Mississippi.

As the icecap retreated farther, Lake Chicago enlarged and Lake Duluth appeared to the north, both still emptying into the Mississippi system. Lake Lundy, succeeding Lake Maumee, now covered a larger area than the present Erie, and its waters flowed east into the Hudson River.

Some fourteen thousand years ago the ice released the escarpment of Niagara, and the waters in the Lake Erie basin turned to pour over the limestone cliffs. The Falls were born, and their long task of cutting the Niagara Gorge began. At present, each year on average the tumbling waters of Niagara eat into the rock something less than four feet, and the gorge is now about seven miles long. In roughly another twenty-five thousand years, if the pattern remained uninterrupted the falls would cut back to a crucial level and *drain Lake Erie*. The spillway of Niagara may not always have occupied its present position; below the escarpment, signs have been found of a buried gorge and buried lower river to the west of the present ones, and they seem to indicate that the river, falls and rapids once followed a very different course.

149

*Figure XXI.*

*Figure XXII.*

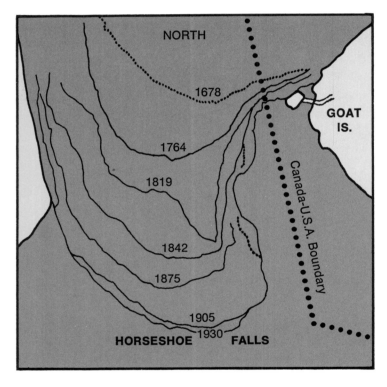

The glacier continued to waste, uncovering all of the Great Lakes Region. Erie remained as the remnant of Lake Lundy; the huge Lake Algonquin covered the entire areas of Superior, Huron and Lake Michigan, its waters pouring eastward through a much enlarged Trent River Valley and the old Mohawk River.

The 'springback' of the land as the ice withdrew caused a succession of drainage changes: at 11,500 BP, only Erie emptied over Niagara Falls, the upper lakes feeding the Trent Valley system; by 11,000 a North Bay outlet had opened, and drainage was through the Mattawa area into the Ottawa River Valley. Then over the next few thousand years, as the land continued to rise the waters turned south to Port Huron.

### Lakes Barlow and Ojibway

The ice recession exposed the Laurentian Upland, a vast area to the north of the Great Lakes, covered by swamps and shallow water. From about 11,000 to 8,000 BP a huge lake of several names and phases covered the region, leaving as its remnants the thousands of lakes in Northern Ontario to-day.

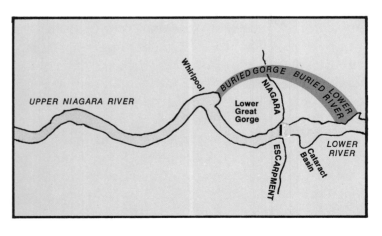

*Figure XIX. Positions of the Horseshoe Falls in years indicated showing rate of cutback by the waters.*

*Figure XX. Niagara River and Gorge, showing buried river and gorge of the ancient spillway.*

150

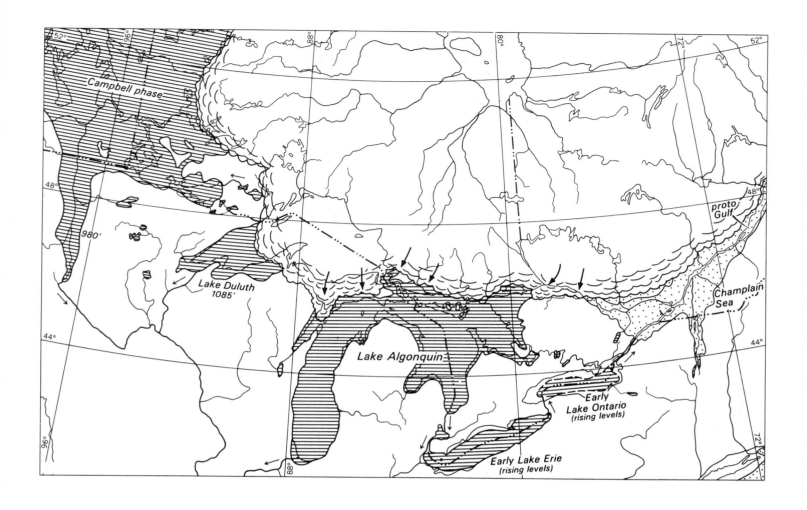

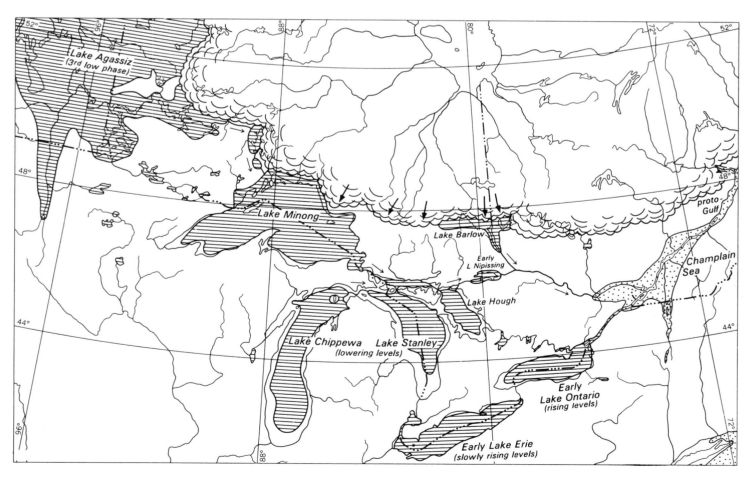

151

*Figure XXIV.*

*Figure XXV.*

## The Champlain Sea*

Over thirteen thousand years ago the Laurentide Glacier withdrew from the St. Lawrence Lowlands and admitted the Atlantic Ocean. The resulting inland body of salt water was the Champlain Sea*, which lay over some twenty thousand square miles of Ontario and Quebec for about four thousand years. Some time before 9,000 BP an uplift west of Quebec City blocked the entry of the ocean, and the Champlain Sea became a salt lake. Later, when an uplift of land to the north took place, the St. Lawrence Valley was raised above sea level; this was the time when the Ottawa River outlet of the Upper Great Lakes was abandoned as their course turned south. The marine waters of the Champlain Sea were expelled, and the present course of drainage established.

*Figure XXIII.*

*\*Also called the "St. Lawrence Sea," by some references.*

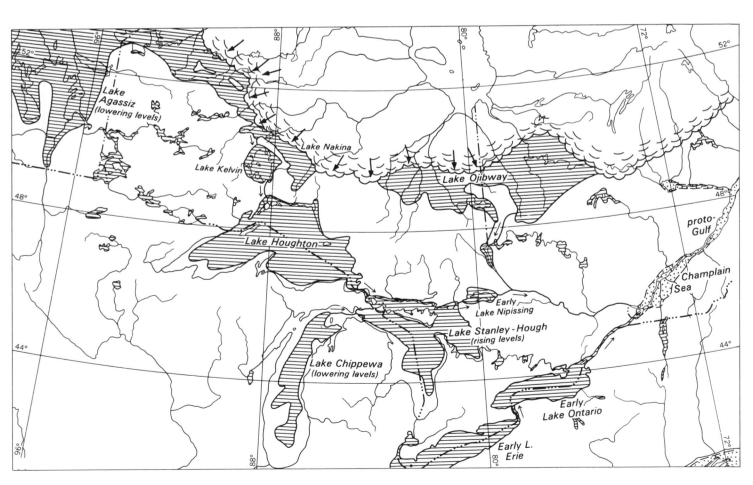

152

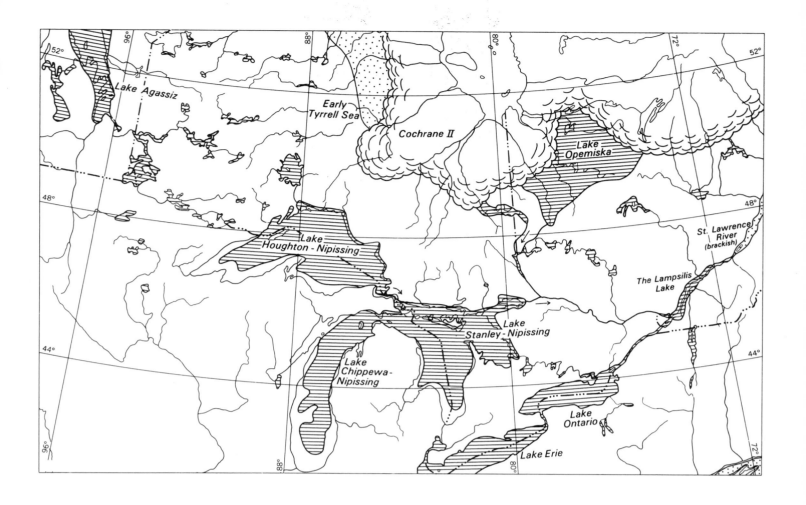

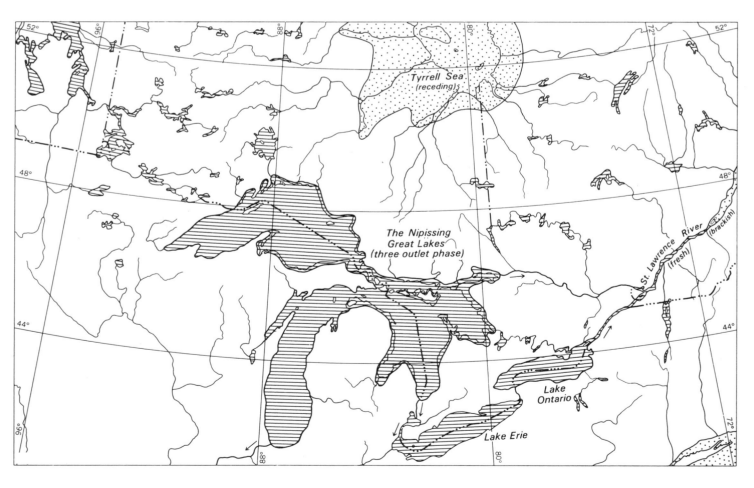

153

*Figure XXVI. Tyrrell Sea, circa 8-7,000 B P.*

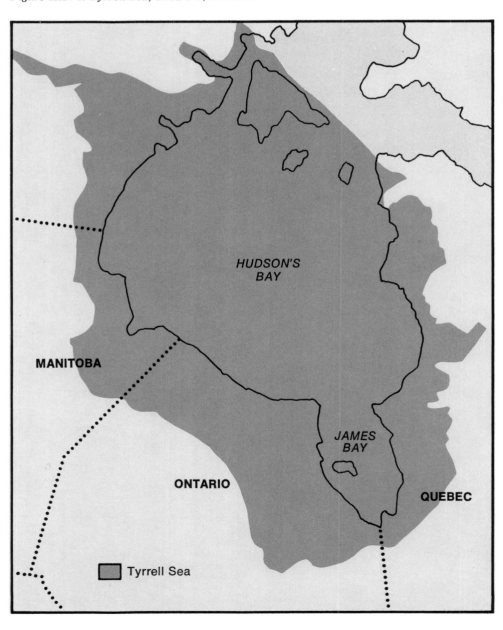

HUDSON'S
BAY

MANITOBA

JAMES
BAY

ONTARIO

QUEBEC

Tyrrell Sea

## Lake Agassiz

Near the time that Lake Duluth was formed, (approximately fourteen thousand years ago,) meltwaters of the retreating ice to the west ponded in an enormous lake of some two hundred thousand square miles. It covered much of Manitoba and extended into Ontario, Saskatchewan, Minnesota and North Dakota. For a time it discharged south into the Mississippi, and in at least one interval, east via the Nipigon Basin. (The fluctuations were caused when the movement of glaciers north of Lake Superior, opened or blocked its eastern outlets.) Then as the land rose its waters turned north to the Tyrrell Sea, or Hudson's Bay; by 7,500-6,700 B P Agassiz had drained out, leaving behind it Lake Winnipeg, Winnipegosis and most of the other lakes of Manitoba and Northern Minnesota.

## The Tyrell Sea

Hudson's Bay can be termed a 'relic' of the Tyrrell, an inland sea that existed during and after deglaciation of the Hudson's Bay Basin. Its high submergence and maximum extent took place about 8,000 to 7,000 B P, when it covered roughly twice the area that is now under marine waters.

When the weight of the Laurentide ice depressed the Hudson's Bay region to a point below sea level, Atlantic waters entered through Hudson's strait to encroach deep on the mainland. The sea water split the icecap at that time, defining two major sheets that lay to the east and west of the Hudson's Bay area.

The waters of Agassiz drained, (and later emptied completely,) into this great sea as the rising land continued its 'springback.' The chronology of the Tyrrell Sea is indistinct; the land is still recovering from the glaciers, and it may be said that the Sea became, "Hudson's Bay," at the time when the upward tilt was sufficient to expel it to the present shorelines. Since the uplift continues, it may be expected that in the next few thousand years Hudson's Bay will be further reduced; if the land returns *entirely* to its former elevation the bay will not exist at all, and Canada's useable land terrain could be increased by almost a half million square miles.

# The Peopling of the Land

*Plate XCVIII. Restoration. Early Man in the Pleistocene.*

# THE FIRST CANADIANS

*The earliest Europeans to reach our shores were true 'discoverers,' if only in the sense that they learned a continent existed in the western sea. They came in ships to lands that were new to them, they explored and they settled. But it was many thousands of years before, that the ancestors of the Indian and Eskimo gravitated across the land bridge to enter a vast new world. They too, were discoverers, who continued the devolution of their own cultures, far removed from 'civilisations' that sprang to life in Europe and Asia.*

## Early Man in North America

In the Tertiary Period there is evidence of three divisions in the ranks of the developing primates,—one of them leading to Man. From the time of earliest Pleistocene as much as five million years ago, relics are found in the old world of a sub-human creature who has been named *Australopithicene.*

Then from six to five hundred thousand years in the past come the earliest traces of *Homo Erectus,* (who includes Java and Peking Man.) In the later period 150,000 to 100,000 B P the Neanderthal, or Mousterian culture appears. The remains of *Neanderthal Man* are found until his apparent extinction some time after fifty thousand years ago, and it is not until then that the first evidence of *Homo Sapiens,* the current species of the human race, becomes clear.

*Homo Erectus* is believed to have been the first 'human being,' gradually beginning to raise himself above the level of the lesser animals. The *Neanderthal* was not a forerunner of Man *but his rival,* for continued evolution to the present human form; he may, however, have been a 'part-ancestor,' and party to the production of a hybrid.

Thus Man, and particularly his brain, has evolved quickly from his earliest recognisable prototype,—in a brief six hundred thousand years or less, while other life forms have generally taken several million. But Darwin and his successors proved beyond any remaining question, that he has emerged through the same laws of Nature that govern all other organisms. And since the last doubt was erased, Man has had to get used to the truth that he does *not* have special significance in the universe,—a task of understanding he has not yet largely accomplished.

Because the primates do not necessarily *culminate* in Man—they only *include* him. He is the result, to this time, of evolutionary processes that have transformed all Life throughout the ages, from the first records of living things in the Precambrian seas. And he has become master of Earth because he alone, of all creatures has not only adapted to his environment but *developed the power to modify it*.

There are opinions that Man, or perhaps *Neanderthal,* did reach the Americas in previous interglacials; a skull *thought* to be neanderthaloid has been unearthed in Brazil. But nothing has been found that would constitute proof. Until further findings it must continue to seem that 'Palaeo-Man,' in the earlier Pleistocene development stages and probably half beast, had not *likely* arrived in North America.

From the Late Sangamon forward however, the findings of archaeology now begin to piece together a very different picture of possibility. At this writing the *fully accepted proof* of human presence on this continent still stands at fifteen thousand years. But very recently that figure was twelve thousand, and only a few years ago, *ten thousand*. With every year of research and discovery the case for a much more ancient history continues to build.

There are some possible evidences of primate evolution in South America during epochs of the Late Tertiary, but they come to a dead end. And the Brazil skull, if it *is* neanderthal, could be over a hundred thousand years old. That age range is also ascribed to the rude artifacts found near Medicine Hat in Alberta,—*if they are truly artifacts*.

In 1961 a geologist working near Taber, Alberta turned up skeleton remains which were first tentatively dated at 22-25,000 B P, then at 40,000. The dating was by stratigraphic relation only and on further investigation was believed older, possibly even over seventy thousand years. But the discovery itself is nebulous, since the skull is that of a child less than two years old, *and is alone*.

At Lewisville, Texas there is an 'Early Man' find which is radiocarbon dated at more than thirty-seven thousand years; but it is not treated as proof because of some discrepancies in the site. On the island of Santa Rosa off California, dates of over thirty thousand years have been obtained on charcoal from hearths, and bones of mammals which appear to have been butchered. At Tule Springs, Arizona there are similar finds, all dated at 25-30,000 B P. Again, the findings are not conclusive enough to be called *evidence*.

MacNeish, (1964,) has written of a tool complex in the Yukon which yielded successive stage dates of 9, 13, and 20-26,000 B P. The ages were determined by deduction only, but crude and questionable artifacts from the Yukon have also been *radiocarbon* dated at some twenty-seven thousand years.

In 1970, archaeological work near the Spectrum Range of Northwestern British Columbia isolated a culture believed to be over twenty-five thousand years old. The objects found have been tentatively correlated with similar sites of the same age in Asia.

Now, in 1971, there is news of a discovery in South America, (again MacNeish,) which has been positively dated, and associates Man with the hunting of sloths about twenty-two thousand years ago.

Lithic tools have been found in a moraine in Michigan, swept down from Canada by a glacier, (presumed the Laurentide during the Wisconsin.) While their age is indeterminate it must be well in excess of fifteen thousand years. And many other finds in the United States point to ages of twenty thousand years and more.

British Columbia's Fraser Canyon was populated twelve thousand years ago. And the only access to that area at that time was from the *South*, indicating a 'retrograde' movement of people who had reached the more southerly regions much earlier.

In Peru a date of 14,000 B P has been obtained on a site of Early Man, and it is logical that a good deal of time—perhaps thousands of years, would have been required for his penetration that far south.

### His Possibilities of Origin

It is now widely believed that two races, or perhaps several varied groups migrated from Asia. Certainly there were at least two markedly different archaeological traditions present in North America before 10,000 B P. The case for *two-way* migration is also well supported. Tolstoy, too, has agreed with this theory. An important factor is that by 9,000 B P the Palaeo-Indians on this continent were producing tools and weapons of a design and technique that is also found in Siberia,—*but not until thousands of years later*. Artifacts from much earlier periods in Asia, on the other hand, are plentiful and they have *no affinity* with anything found in Canada.

The first Late Wisconsin opening of the land bridge was before 40,000 B P, and there *may* have been some sparse migration at that time. However, there is a distinct type of human lithic culture that dates from forty thousand years and more in the past; artifacts from it have been widely documented in Eurasia. But at this date not one verified trace of it has ever been turned up in North America. In short the question of the earlier migrations is still a question, and an open one.

Even more controversial is the insistence of a few American scholars that Man, evolving bilaterally in the warmer regions of the South, came to Canada as a northern explorer of *his own* continent. They intimate that the mongoloid features of some early northern inhabitants may be only *descriptively* and perhaps not *congenitally* mongoloid. Or—were the northern Indian tribes, (who distinctly differentiate in features from the southern tribes and South Americans,) original migrant Mongols, conveniently bastardised by a few fun-loving adventurers from a continentally indigenous race to the south?

We admit at least that the self-thinker can turn to a broadening of the intrigues presented by continental drift, the Supercontinent Pangaea, and a *possible* American evolution of humanoid life from the lower forms. Many American findings point to Mongol-Caucasoid *hybrid* indicators—in some tribes and peoples *and not in others*. But we must also return to the fact that in the old world there is evidence of Man's evolution *every step of the way,* and in the Americas there is nothing, except a few remote signs of a primate development in the Tertiary which appears to have died out.

There is also conjecture that the 'Amerind,' (American Indian,) *invented* his culture, and that late-coming immigrants were peacefully absorbed into it. Archaeology finds some sign of Man killing Man on a planned and orderly basis, but the activity is not intense until much later, when ever-developing standards and the inroads of Europeans created one factor heretofore absent—ambition. But why then was this continent so sparsely populated when the Europeans arrived? It does not suggest long years of growth by a native race, unless that race was weak and far from prolific. Again it must constitute logic that the best explanations for these 'multiple types and cultures', lie in natural dispersal, successive waves of migration and divisions of type in Asia before the migrations took place. One type, the northern Mongols, were the precursors of Eskimo, Aleut and Athapascan. Another race from the more southerly regions of Asia were probably the earlier migrants,—people with features much like most native Canadians and Americans have to-day.

Glottochronology, the science of dating languages, is based on the time required for their divergence. Groups isolated from a mother-tongue lose about 19% of its morphemes each thousand years. And all of the tribal languages spoken in North and South America have had time to diffuse from a single tongue or two tongues—much in keeping with the pattern of arrivals that seems most obvious.

## A Sangamon Canadian?

The glaciers so effectively bulldozed everything in their path that there is much we may never know about the Sangamon. While Canada four times suffered total glaciation the United States did not, except for a small northern portion of her territory. There *could* have been humanoid life in Canada over a hundred thousand years ago, moving south as the ice advanced. The glacier would not have destroyed the people,—only the evidence of their passing.

The theory is weak, mainly because no interglacial-dated remains have been found in the United States. But Man in North America *was* south of the ice before 12,000 B P,—that much is proven. Was he also then *north* of the forty-ninth parallel before the Wisconsin advance? Again, the elusive but possible 'Sangamon Canadian'.

If he did exist he was of a 'wanderer' culture,— *Neanderthal, Homo Erectus* or both, and his penetration into this continent limited to small nomadic bands of hunters or family groups following the movements of a given source of food. There were herds of mammoth and bison in the interglacial, for him to have preyed upon. And his presence, if ever fully proven would resolve at last the haunting half-evidence of a race that may have been here and long established when later migrants arrived.

## His Probable Migrations

While the time beyond 40,000 B P remains shrouded in doubt, the Asian technologies for the *next* land bridge period, (beginning about twenty-eight thousand years ago,) *are* duplicated in North American findings. Groups of hunters crossed Beringia at that time, probably making both continents common ground for up to five thousand years.

Then there was an interval some twenty-five thousand years ago, in which average temperatures cooled with glacial readvances, some of the land ecology hunters moved southward in Asia, and also in North America through the Rocky Mountain Corridor route. The predominantly Mongoloid marine-hunters stayed in the North, maintaining contact with the evolving Siberian peoples, as all artifacts attest. The distinct culture definitions of the North and South were inevitable, since the groups then became isolated from each other for many thousands of years. To support this conclusion, artifacts in the South correlate with those of Siberia twenty-eight thousand years ago, *but not with later developments of the Siberian culture;* those in the North however, show an almost unbroken affinity between the two continents until about 10,000 B P. At the end of the Pleistocene, re-contact with the northern people was made by Palaeo-Indians spreading northward again with the retreating ice, as those who had remained in the ice-free areas of Alaska and the Yukon, gravitated south. Only a few years ago this time was accepted as the earliest presence of Man in North America.

The older dates are supported but unproven. The younger and more conservative, such as 15,000 B P, are proven but beset with many contributing factors that indicate they are *too* conservative. Now, in the light of *all* findings it seems possible to sum up these theories: that there was no human evolution in the Americas; that there may have been migration over forty thousand years ago; that there *was* migration at twenty-eight to twenty-three thousand years ago, and again from thirteen to ten thousand; that there has been time for all the native ethnic groups to diverge from one people and language stock; that the peopling of North America took place in either two or three waves, at the distinct times when the Bering Bridge stood dry; and that diffusion into the present tribal and linguistic elements was accomplished not only on this continent, but also bilaterally in Asia.

## Breaking the Code

One reason for the great gaps in knowledge of Early Man in Canada, is that Canadian archaeology is young; extensive work has begun only in the last few years. Most of the findings have not yet been published, and there is still great difficulty in obtaining equipment and funds. But another major reason is lack of communication, and in particular the regrettable practice of scholars in introducing new names representing complexes, focal groups, industries, traditions, phases, sub-phases and cultures for practically every 'find' or individual site that is encountered.

The resulting confusion baffles even professionals, and in the interest of some defence against this 'Canadian Small Paper Tradition' the following lists have been prepared. Some explanation is offered of the maze of bewildering names and terms that the amateur reader in Canadian prehistory will encounter, and surely there are many more than it has been possible to include here. Most important to simplicity is the matter of assembling them into the four major time divisions recognised in the story of Canadian population movements and life patterns.

*It is important to remember that Canadian and American archaeology are irrevocably linked together, since Early Man knew of no 'boundaries' that were later to separate nations or sovereign states.*

## Table V

I. FROM EARLIEST OCCUPATIONS TO 7,500 B P  (PALAEO-INDIAN PERIOD)

| TERM | CORRELATION (and approximate time) (associations—all dates) (are years Before Present) |
|---|---|
| AGATE BASIN | Plano |
| ALBERTA | Cody |
| ANGOSTURA | Plano, Agate Basin |
| CASCADE | Old Cordilleran |
| CLOVIS | Llano. General term. First fully developed North American Culture. Western Plains. Dates average 12-11,000 |
| CODY COMPLEX | Clovis, Folsom, Agate Basin, Scotsbluff, Eden, Alberta. Plains, mostly Colorado, Wyoming, Alberta, Montana. 9,000-8,500 |
| CORDILLERAN TRADITION | Plano. Northern Rockies, Northwest Territories, Yukon. 9,000-7,000 |
| CRESCENT | California |
| DENALI | Arctic |
| DESERT CULTURE | Great Basin. Small game hunters. Leads to Shoshone. |
| EARLY PREHISTORIC | General term. 12,000-7,000 |
| EDEN | Cody |
| EPI-CLOVIS | obscure term. Clovis period and type |
| EPI-GRAVETTIAN | Old-world term. Late Gravettian. 20,000 |
| FLINT CREEK | Cordilleran Tradition. NWT (Mackenzie Delta) 9,000-7,000 |
| FOLSOM | general term, plains, Western North America. Type site at Folsom, N. Mexico. 11,000-7,000 |
| FREDERICK | obscure term. Plains. 7,000 |
| GRAVETTIAN | Old-world term. 25,000-20,000 |
| HELL GAP | Plano. & Variation of Agate Basin. Wyoming, Alberta. Type site in Wyoming. 10,000-9,500 |
| INTERMONTANE | Western mountains |
| KLONDIKE | Cordilleran Tradition. S.W. Mackenzie. 8,000 |
| KLUANE | Southwest Yukon |
| LERMA | Old Cordilleran |
| LIND COULEE | Plano. Old Cordilleran. E. Washington |
| LITHIC | Stone cutlures, usually early |
| LITTLE GEM | Local, Eastern Alberta |
| LONG | Agate Basin, Angostura, Black Hills, Dakotas |
| LUSK | Angostura |

164

| | |
|---|---|
| MESERVE | late. Eastern United States |
| MIDLAND | unfluted Folsom |
| MILNESAND | Cody |
| MOHAVE | Lake Mohave. S. California & Nevada |
| MOUNDBUILDERS | Manitoba. Lake Aggasiz |
| MOUNTAIN-PLAINS | obscure term. West. |
| NORTHERN PLANO | late phase deviation term for Plano |
| NORTHERN POINT TRADITION | NWT and Arctic |
| OID CORDILLERAN | Plano. Lerma. Northwest America |
| PALAEOLITHIC | Old-world term. Oldest stone cultures. 1.000.000 to 40,000 |
| PASIKA | Arctic |
| PELLY | Agate Basin, Northern Plano. Arctic. |
| PLAINVIEW | Midland. unfluted Folsom. Texas |
| PLANO | general type. Continental. 10,000-5,000 |
| PROTO-ARCHAIC | N. American. same as old-world 'Proto-Meso-lithic' |
| PROTO-ATHAPASCAN | leads to Athapascans. Prior to 6,000 |
| PROTO-MESOLITHIC | old-world term. Period of transitions from no-madic to sedentary life. |
| SANDIA | general type. Oldest. Continental. 14,000-15,000 and earlier |
| SCOTSBLUFF | Cody |
| TAIGAN | tundra, boreal forest hunters. 10,000-7,500 |

# Table VI

II. 7,500 TO 1,500 B P
(Meso-Indian Period)

| TERM | CORRELATION (and approximate time ) (associations—all dates ) (are years Before Present) |
|---|---|
| ALEUT TRADITION | Aleutian Islands. 5,000 to present |
| ARCHAIC | general term. 7,000-2,000 |
| ARCTIC SMALL TOOL TRADITION | leads to Eskimo. 5,700-2,000 |
| ARTILLERY LAKE | Yuma Tradition. NWT. 5,000 |
| ATHAPAP | Northwest |
| AVONLEA | Besant. 1,900-1,200. Also Neo Period |
| BAKER'S NARROWS | Manitoba, north. (Shield) |
| BESANT | Sask., S. Alberta, Montana, Dakotas. Type site Besant Valley, Sask. 1,900-1,300. Leads to Algonkian |
| BITTEROOT | N.W. Plains & mountains. 7,500-5,000. Leads to Shoshone |
| BROOKS RIVER | Northwest, Arctic |
| CATHEDRAL | West Coast. 3.000. Leads to Bella Coola and related tribes |
| CHAMPAGNE | Yuma Tradition. NWT & Yukon. 6,000 |
| CHORIS | INUK Tradition. Arctic. over 3,000 |
| DENBIGH FLINT COMPLEX | Arctic Small Tool Tradition. 5,000 |
| DENETASIRO TRADITION | NWT, Yukon, Alaska. 2,000 to present |
| DISMAL LAKES | YUMA. NWT. 5,000-4,000. Leads to Athapascan. |
| DISMAL RIVER | Western Nebraska. Late Period |
| DORSET TRADITION | Arctic. 3,000-1,000. Leads to Dorset Eskimo |
| DUNCAN | follows McKean. Same area. 4,000 |
| EARLY ARCHAIC | general term. 7,000-4,000 |
| EARLY WOODLAND | eastern. 2,000-1,700. Leads to Iroquois |
| EVANS | obscure term. (Plains?) |
| FISHERMAN'S LAKE | Northwest Microblade Tradition. N.W.T. 3,000 |
| FRANKLIN TANKS | YUMA Tradition. NWT. 6,500 |
| GREAT BEAR RIVER | YUMA Tradition. NWT. 5,000 |
| HANNA | as Duncan. 3,500 |
| INDEPENDENCE | Arctic Small Tool Tradition. 4,000 |
| INUK TRADITION | Alaska, NWT. 4,300 to present. Leads to Eskimo |
| IPIUTAK | INUK Tradition. 1,800 |
| KACHEMAK (I, II & III) | North Pacific Tradition. Gulf of Alaska. 3,500-1,500 |
| LAMOKAN | Upstate New York. Early. Precedes Iroquois. |
| LARTER | Manitoba, 1,500 and earlier. Leads to Algonkian |
| LATE ARCHAIC | general term. 4,000-2,000 |
| LAUREL TRADITION | Eastern Woodlands. Leads to Iroquois |
| LAURENTIAN | Eastern. Leads to Algonkian |
| LAURENTIAN ARCHAIC | Eastern. Late Algonkian |
| LITTLE ARM | Northwest Microblade Tradition. S.W. Mac-kenzie. 6,000-5,500 |
| LOCKHART RIVER | Northwest Microblade Tradition. NWT. 3,500-3,000. Leads to Athapascan |
| LONG CREEK | Saskatchewan. Oxbow Complex. Leads to Algonkian |
| MARITIME ARCHAIC | Archaic. Cultures Labrador to Northern New England. Leads to Iroquois |
| MARPOLE PHASE | Strait of Georgia. 1,600 and earlier |
| McKEAN | Northern Plains. 5,000-4,000 |

| | |
|---|---|
| MIDDLE ALEUT | Aleutians, 2,000 |
| MIDDLE PREHISTORIC | general term, 7,000-2,000 |
| MIDDLE WOODLAND | Eastern Woodlands. 1700-1200. Also Neo Period |
| MOOREHEAD CEMETERY | Archaic. Maine and Maritimes |
| MORTLACH | Saskatchewan, Besant Valley, also Neo Period. Leads to Algonkian |
| MUMMY CAVE | Wyoming. Pre-Shoshone. Older—probably Palaeo-Period |
| NESIKEP TRADITION | Interior British Columbia. 2,500. Leads to Thompson Indians. |
| NEW BRUNSWICK ARCHAIC | late Algonian |
| NORTHERN POINT TRADITION | Boreal Forest |
| NORTH PACIFIC TRADITION | Gulf of Alaska. 5,000 to present |
| NORTHWEST MICROBLADE TRADITION | Northwestern British Columbia and Northern Plateau, NWT. Arctic. 6,500-2,000. Leads to Athapascans |
| NORTON | INUK Tradition. 2,000-1,500 |
| OKVIK | INUK Tradition. 2,500-2,000 |
| OXBOW | Saskatchewan and plains. 5,000-4,500 |
| OLD BERING SEA | INUK Tradition. 2,000-1,500 |
| OLD COPPER CULTURE | Eastern Woodlands. 7,000-2,000 |
| OLD WHALING | leads to Eskimo |
| PALAEO-ALEUT | Aleutians. 3,000 |
| PALISADES | Arctic. Leads to Eskimo |
| PELICAN LAKE | Saskatchewan. 3,500-1,500. Leads to Algonkian |
| POINTED MOUNTAIN | Northwest Microblade Tradition. NWT. 4,500 |
| PRE-DORSET | Arctic. 4,000. Leads to Dorset |
| PROTO-ATHAPASCAN | Early Meso Period. Leads to Athapascan |
| PROTO-DORSET | forerunner of Dorset and Pre-Dorset |
| SANDY CREEK | Saskatchewan. Mortlach. 2,000 |
| SANDY LAKE | Yuma Tradition. NWT. 6,000 |
| SECURITY COVE | Arctic |
| SHIELD ARCHAIC | Manitoba. 7,000-6,000. Leads to Algonkian |
| SIGNAL BUTTE | McKean. Nebraska. Leads to Siouian |
| THUNDER CREEK | Saskatchewan. Mortlach. 3,400. Leads to Algonkian |
| TRANSITIONAL | obscure term. Probably period after Altithermal |
| TUNAXA | Northwest Plains. 4,000-1,000. Leads to Algonkian—Blackfoot |
| UNCOMPAHGRE | area term. Colorado and Plateau. Leads to Uto-Aztecan |
| WHITESHELL | Manitoba. To Algonkian |

| | |
|---|---|
| WOOD END | Long Creek |
| YUMA TRADITION | NWT and Yukon. 7,000-4,500 |

## Table VII

III. 1,500 TO 500 BP
(Neo-Indian Period)

| TERM | CORRELATION (associations—all dates (and approximate time are years Before Present) |
|---|---|
| ALGONKIAN | Leading to tribes of Algonkian origin |
| ALEUT TRADITION | see Meso Period, overlap |
| ANDERSON | Manitoba. Southern grasslands. 500. To Algonkian |
| ARCTIC WOODLAND | obscure term. Probably tundra Indian |
| ATHAPASCAN | (or Athabaskan). Leading to tribes of Athapascan origin |
| AVONLEA | see Meso Period, overlap |
| BESANT | see Meso Period, overlap |
| CARON | Saskatchewan. Mortlach. 1,200 and later |
| CLEARWATER LAKE | Manitoba, (North). Ceramics |
| DENETASIRO TRADITION | see Meso Period, overlap |
| DORSET TRADITION | see Meso Period, overlap |
| ESKIMOAN | leading to tribes of Eskimoan origin |
| HOPEWELL | agricultural society, Eastern Woodlands 1,800 and later. Eastern U.S. (Ohio) probably extended into Canada |
| INTERMOUNTAIN | Western mountains. 1,000. Pottery |
| INUK TRADITION | see Meso Period, overlap |
| IROQUOIAN | leading to tribes of Iroquoian origin |
| KACHEMAK III and IV | North Pacific Tradition. 1,500-500 |
| KAMLOOPS PHASE | Cultures leading to Salish |
| KWATNA | West Coast. Bella Coola and related tribes |
| LATE PLAINS | Southern plains. 1,700-500 |
| LATE PREHISTORIC | general term. 1,500-500 |
| LATE WOODLAND | Eastern Woodlands. 1,200-1,000 |
| MANITOBA | Manitoba southern grasslands. 1,000-500. Leads to Algonkian |
| MIDDLE WOODLAND | see Meso Period, overlap |
| MORTLACH | see Meso Period, overlap |

| | |
|---|---|
| NAPIKWAN | Northwest plains. 1,000-500. Algonkian—Blackfoot |
| NEO-ALEUT | forerunner to present Aleut |
| NORTH PACIFIC TRADITION | see Meso Period, overlap |
| NUKLEET | Arctic |
| NUTIMIK | Southwestern Manitoba |
| PLAINS SIDE-NOTCH | weapon point type. 1,300 |
| PLAINS TRIANGULAR | weapon point type. 1,300 |
| PRINCESS POINT COMPLEX | Late Woodland. L. Ontario and L. Erie region. Leads to Ontario Iroquois Tradition |
| PROTO-HISTORIC | prior to 500 |
| PUNUK | INUK Tradition. 1,000 |
| SELKIRK | Manitoba grasslands. 500. Leads to Algonkian |
| TUNAXA | see Meso Period, overlap |
| THULE | Arctic. (late.) 1,000. Leads to present Eskimo |
| WHITEFISH LAKE | Denetasiro Tradition. Mackenzie District. 1,000 and later |

## Table VIII

IV. 500 BP TO PRESENT
(The Historic Period)

| TERM | CORRELATION (and approximate time associations—all dates are years Before Present) |
|---|---|
| ALL CURRENT TRIBAL NAMES | names generally used 500 to present |
| CARON | Saskatchewan. (Mortlach). Also Neo Period, overlap |
| CONTACT | time of Euro-American influence |
| DENETASIRO TRADITION | see Meso Period, overlap |
| EYAK | North Pacific Tradition. Recent. |
| INUGSUK | INUK Tradition. 500 |
| INUK TRADITION | see Meso Period, overlap |
| LATE PLAINS SIDE-NOTCHED | general term for arrowheads. 500 and later |
| MOOSE JAW | Southern Saskatchewan, Alberta and Manitoba. Long Creek or Mortlach site types |
| NORTHERN PACIFIC TRADITION | see Meso Period, overlap |
| ONTARIO IROQUOIS TRADITION | Eastern Woodlands. 500 to recent |
| TRADE METAL | general term, materials obtained from Europeans. Dates average 350 and later. |

*Plate XCIX. Animals hunted by the Palaeo-Indian.*

## The Palaeo-Indian Period

As the successive migrations brought him to the new world, Man moved sporadically south and east, eventually inhabiting all of North, South and Central America. With the exception of the Corridor areas and the far Northwest, his arrivals in Canada began in the East. Rather than to cross the still-frozen western plains, some peoples skirted the ice margin and established a forest hunting culture in the eastern woodlands. As the glaciers withdrew they extended their territory to part of Ontario, Quebec and the Maritimes.

Other groups continued southward from the Corridor route, and still others turned to the West through mountain passes, or remained to inhabit the Great Basin and American Central Plains. Most of the earliest migrants, probably for climatic reasons, had remained in the Southwestern United States and Mexico, (people of the Sandia and Llano Cultures.) Now, as temperatures moderated they trended north again, increasing the population on the plains; still later, as the ice receded, many of their number dispersed into Canada, to infiltrate Southern British Columbia and the lower prairies, while at the same time migrant arrivals continued from the North.

In Alaska and the Aleutians all evidences show a distinctly *separate* culture from the beginning. There are many indications that the majority of North American Eskimos were among the *latest* migrants from Asia. Now a fully developed Arctic-Mongoloid stock, they penetrated into Alaska. Because of their sea-hunting economy and life-style, they quickly spread eastward through the Canadian Arctic as far as Greenland, rather than to gravitate south to the interior as the Palaeo-Indians had done.

The Post-Pleistocene occupation of most areas, seems practically as early as the ice withdrawals: in the East, from 15,000 B P; on the plains, from an average 13,000; Southern British Columbia and the coast, about 12,000. There are much older dates in the far northern areas that remained ice-free, while the boreal forest zones bear Early Man dates of only seven to nine thousand years, and the Aleutians show little sign of human presence until about eight thousand years ago.

The environment of the plains has changed only superficially in the last hundred centuries, and there the earliest movements of Man have been as much concerned with distance as with ecology. The first settlings in Manitoba were on the western shores of Lake Aggasiz, and advanced as far north as the Swan River Valley. Then there seems to have been a terminal phase of occupation after 8,000 B P, when the hunters moved westward, probably because of drought conditions. The time coincides with the period when Aggasiz would have been completely drained out to the north.

There is little if any Palaeo-Indian record in the northern woodlands of Manitoba and Saskatchewan, and in the far north tundra it is sparse,—a few spearpoints dating 9,000-8,500, about the time that the ice had receded that far to the north and east.

Alberta and Southern Saskatchewan were continually occupied, though in the boreal forest belt to the

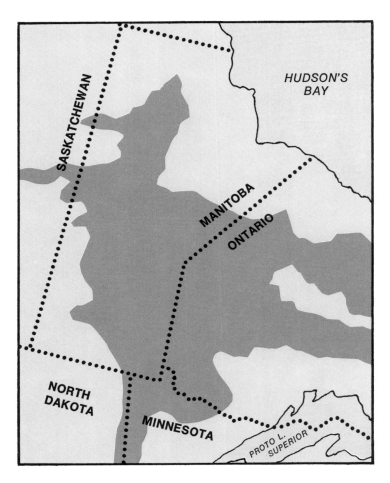

Figure XXVII. Glacial Lake Agassiz, circa 10,000 B P.

north of present Edmonton the population was light, in keeping with the severity of a single-mammal hunting style by men on foot. In the southern interior of British Columbia the influx was from the south until about the end of the period, when arrivals began from the north and east. These latter were the ancestors of the Interior Salish, a people who are there to this day.

The West Coast, Strait of Georgia, and Gulf Islands were populated from 12,000 B P, earliest settlings taking place in the Fraser Canyon. On the Queen Charlottes there were groups that reached the region on dry land, then became isolated about ten to eight thousand years ago as the sea levels rose.

The Clovis Hunters from the south, as they moved into the Canadian plains and foothills may have brought with them the skills of communal buffalo hunting, a practice which was to infinitely alter the life-style of the Plains Indian. It also seems there was some migration from the plains to the plateaux of Southern British Columbia, beginning about twelve thousand years ago.

Early people of the West had little defence against Canadian winters, and annual movements to places of climatic refuge were common. Typical of these sheltered havens are the narrows in Waterton National Park; they are kept free of snow and ice the year round by prevailing Chinook winds, and were a seasonal mecca for tribes of both plains and mountains. Western Indians reached them by the South Kootenay and Flathead Passes through the Rockies, and the many bands of plains dwellers who came there each year are evidenced by tools and weapons of materials which were not local, but from the Dakotas, Wyoming, Montana and elsewhere.

The Palaeo-Indians were seldom cave-dwellers; until they had learned to devise shelters they lived in the open, often sleeping between fires for warmth and protection. While the major *area* groups continued their gradual delineation, some aspects of their cultures were common throughout the land. The earliest comers led an indescribably harsh life, and lived on what game they could take, their primitive hunting techniques not often rewarded with the prize of a large mammal. There were none of the warring patterns, coups or tribal conflicts so well known to recent history; the first Canadians were much too concerned with eking out an existence to fight among themselves.

Their large game consisted of mastodon, mammoth in some areas, muskox, and on the great plains an extinct form of early bison. Life was heavily influenced by changing geographic features, such as Lake Aggasiz in Manitoba and the lesser glacial lakes that were scattered from coast to coast. Competition from large predators,—the Alaskan lion, dire wolves and the developing forms of modern-day bears, added to the complexity of simply staying alive.

Most of the huge Late Pleistocene grazing mammals were well protected. The great tusks of the mastodon and plains mammoth, like the raking points of the long-horned bison were no mean armament, and the claws of the giant sloth could rip a log apart like paper. But above all, the sheer size and weight of these creatures must have placed the early Palaeo-Indian at a tremendous disadvantage. Before the atlatl and bow he had only his intelligence and

Plate C.

Plate CI. Atlatl.

the crude weapons he had devised, as 'levellers.' The taking of a mammoth with spears amounted to little less than close-quarters combat, and Man did not always emerge the victor. Even more probable is the suggestion that he rarely *tried*, contenting himself with the smaller game he could bring down; and that his access to the heavy mammals was limited largely to their young or injured, until co-operative hunting and more advanced weapons came into being.

And surely the later inventions of tools which could kill at a distance, were hardly the result of any *sudden* flash of inspiration. For thousands of years Early Man must have gazed into his fires after days when his prowess had yielded only roots and berries, a gnawing hunger driving his human brain to search for a method; a way to acquire in safety the food he saw all about him,—but food that was too swift, and food that was too powerful.

The spear was his first projectile, and the accuracy with which it was used is attested by the very fact of his survival. But it had no range, and only the force of a weak human arm behind it,—still little more than a hand weapon. Then, in the period from ten to eight thousand years ago, a weapon appeared which could have been brought by the latest wave of migrants, or invented by the Palaeo-Indian himself. The device was a two-to-three foot long 'launching handle', used to propel a short, sharp spear. And the effect was to 'lengthen' the thrower's arm, improving both range and striking impact. It was later modified by addition of a weight stone, again increasing the force behind the throw. As an advance in technology

the *Atlatl* was rude and elementary—but for the first time, Man was equipped to kill without placing himself in reach of his quarry's defences.

The centuries wore on, the animal populations changed, and each succeeding generation adapted more closely to its regional environs. The people of the northern forests subsisted on a varied diet which included moose, caribou and wood buffalo as well as small game. The supply, again, was difficult to take and not dependable, effectively limiting not only Man's numbers in the boreal wilderness, but his cultural momentum as well.

The plains, as hunting skills developed, were very much in contrast; the new-participants of communal effort found that large herds of buffalo could easily be taken through the use of 'pounds' and 'jumps'. Soon their economy was fully geared to the bison. Meat in plenty, an abundance of berries, and preservation methods such as drying and pemmican resulted in a 'plains stability',—a people without fear of starvation. Their number increased, and the leisure presented by absence of want permitted a rapid structuring of their society and their traditions of ritualism.

In the eastern woodlands the inexhaustible bison herds were unknown, and the Palaeo-Indians of the great forests became the finest hunters on Earth. Until the extinctions their diet still included many creatures of the Ice Age—mastodon, sloth and horse, Irish elk and others, but as the Altithermal approached the varieties of wildlife became limited to those of the present. Their food supply, as before, was not predictable and a diet reliance on plants came into their culture. Crushers and grinding stones are found from more than eight thousand years ago, and by the time the first Europeans reached the Great Lakes the eastern Indians were using over four hundred plant species for food, medicine and smoking.

The plains people seem at first to have had no dwellings, then as collective hunting practices develop there are tipi-rings and multi-family encampments. The groups living together usually numbered fifty to a hundred or more, and there is evidence of religious activity; flexed burials, (positioned with the knees drawn up against the chest,) contain red ochre and personal belongings, and in many sites fires had been built over them. The artifacts and weapons found show essentially the same living habits in Alberta, Saskatchewan and Manitoba. Settlements were numerous and they increase rapidly as younger dates are encountered, suggesting a highly prolific buildup of population wherever the buffalo ranged.

No people ever utilised the varied substances of Nature more totally than the prehistoric Canadians. Even in the Palaeo-Indian stage their choice of materials was remarkably discriminate. Tools and weapons of stone were always made from rock types that take and hold the best edge,—cherts such as jasper, flint, agate and quartzite; in the West, obsidian was a favourite material, a natural black volcanic glass which the Indians travelled long distances to acquire. Their 'quarries' were usually accompanied by 'workshop' sites, where implements were shaped before they set out on the return journey.

Obsidian artifacts are widely found, but in the far Northwest are associated with dates of fifteen, twenty thousand years and more. In the interior of Alaska the *Batza Tena* "Obsidian Trail," has been frequented by hunter groups from Palaeo times almost to the present. The glass was created by vulcanism in the Mid-Tertiary, and the Indians there today recognise it in their past culture, still using small blades to open blisters caused by snow-blindness. Obsidian, when 'spalls' or flakes are struck from a main block, produces a razor sharp edge that will dress out a deer carcass more efficiently than the finest Sheffield steel. Palaeo-Indian sites in Alaska are often in the mountains; 'chipping stations' are common, usually high on a hilltop overlooking a river valley, where hunters perched at their vantage point making weapons, and scanned the valley floor below for game.

The people of the Arctic pursued a totally different economy. Where the early Indian made artifacts of stone, the Eskimo used bone and ivory. When dwellings were built, large sections of whale bone served the same structural purpose as wood provided to the forest dwellers. The Eskimo and Aleut, together with Bering Sea Mongoloids on the Asiatic side, have evolved their marine hunting and transport methods from earliest times. At first they used skins to build simple coracles*—then later the *Umiak,* (a coracle with a keelson). Finally they devised the *Kayak,* a masterpiece of engineering which made possible

*open boats

hunting in the open sea, out of sight of land, and broadened at once the user's food supply and his territory.

On the central west coast there is evidence of occupation from about 8,000 B P, where a generally maritime economy has existed in all periods. The ancestors of the Bella Coola, Bella Bella and related tribes built pithouse villages in the fjord country of the mainland, and appear to have only seasonally inhabited the ocean shore and island sites. Theirs was a fishing society, with no apparent shortage of food, with early ritualisms, and a range of artifacts which do not readily identify with those of coastal Indians to the south.

The Georgia Straits, Gulf Islands, Fraser Delta and adjacent inland areas were settled from terminal Pleistocene times, by a people whose economy has been traditionally inseparable from the salmon. Whatever other game has complemented their existence, the 'king of fish' has always provided the predictable plenty that later gave rise to the most renowned art and highly structured Indian societies in Canada.

Before the faunal extinctions, the animals contemporary with Early Man presented a fascinating variety; several of them could readily have been adapted as beasts of burden, which would instantly have altered the course of Canadian history. Both camels and horses were part of the Palaeo-Indian's diet. But it never occurred to him to ride them rather than to eat them,—the species vanished, and Man on this continent remained a pedestrian until the re-intro-duction of the horse, little more than four hundred years ago.

As the period opened, languages had not diffused a great deal except for the effect of the early 'north-south' separations. By the end of Palaeo-Indian times they had probably undergone their division into six major groups, beginning to form the basic area tongues of the Arctic, eastern woodlands, Northwest, central interior, southern plains, and western mountain-coastal regions.

With the sweeping change in faunal varieties and climate, the total hunting cultures of the Ice Age had given way to diversity. Food and environment were the influences that shaped their ways of life, the nomadic patterns of their ancestors were discarded, and tribes and nations began to emerge as 'rightful occupants' of their hereditary hunting lands.

*Plate CII. Buffalo jump.*

## The Meso-Indian Period

The latest Palaeo-Indian years had been a time of 'settling-in.' More than a hundred generations had passed since the last movements from Asia, and a now-native people held only in dim memory the handed-down sagas of long journeys.

But their ethnic grouping, at first related only to geography, was now again profoundly affected,—by the Altithermal. For some two thousand years, all the land suffered drought. The plains were parched and dry, the buffalo scarce, and the hunters were drawn toward less arid regions to the north and east. The slim population of the prairies centred on lake fringes, rivers and streams. People in the desert interior of British Columbia crossed the Rockies into the northern tundra, and there was scattered migration to the eastern woodlands, where more moderate conditions prevailed.

At about 5,000 B P the climatic trend shifted, weather and seasons gradually becoming much as we know them to-day. The buffalo herds increased on the plains again, and the Meso-Indian population grew with them. Reoccupation in large numbers seems to have come from all directions, and the bison-oriented economy, by Neo-Indian times numbered its members in the hundreds of thousands.

All the cultures of Canada now began a more distinct development; the herd-hunters and fishermen tribes in the West, the forest-hunters and maize-growers of the East,—while in the frozen wastelands of the North, both Eskimo and Indian continued their ancient and time-tested customs.

*Plate CIII.*

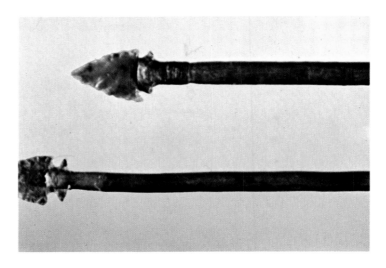

The bow and arrow came into use, easily the Meso-Indian's greatest single advance in weaponry. Its appearance is recognised at more than two thousand years ago, but might possibly have been *four to six thousand*. Organic relics such as wooden bows and shafts are rarely found, and many of the earlier projectile points believed to be those of atlatl spears, could as readily be arrowheads. Whether the bow originated on this continent will never be surely known. But the weapons of the entire period were more sophisticated in North America than in other parts of the world. And there was continuous contact with Asia through the Eskimo, whose advanced kayak navigated the Bering Strait with ease. It seems highly likely that the invention of the bow was given to the world by the North American Indian.

It is also both interesting and puzzling that the Meso-Canadians did not develop their own 'bronze age'. In the Lake Superior Region pure copper nuggets were to be found, malleable and easily worked into various shapes. Cold and hot, they were hammered into arrow and spear points, ornaments, axes and knives for thousands of years. But the Indians also continued to make stone artifacts, and then for some reason turned away from the copper lore.

In the Arctic, the Eskimo had perfected his marine hunting techniques almost as they stand to the present. His housing, always versatile, now included sod winter dwellings and skin tents as well as the snowhouse. The Aleuts had separated as a people and a language stock, by 5,000 B P, and the main Eskimo strain inhabited all of the Arctic maritime regions from Alaska to Labrador. By three to four thousand years ago, some of them had penetrated as far south as Northeastern Manitoba, where there are still settlements on the shores of Hudson's Bay.

The Indians of the northern territories, never numerous, favoured a nomadic, single-family style of subsistence throughout the period. Their small 'villages' are mostly winter sites, and there was little of any form of organised society. Well into the permafrost zone, they dug pits for houses and food-caches, and relied heavily on the individual hunting of caribou, fish and small game. They were Northern Athapascans, who at three to four thousand years ago were still largely one ethnic group, excepting the Tlingit Indians of the west coast, who separated to form their own culture at about 6,000 B P.

Vulcanism continued in part of British Columbia. In the Northwest, both Tahltan and Tsimshian lore

178

Plate CIV. "House-pits,"—sites of ancient pithouse villages found in the British Columbia interior.

Figure XXVIII. Plan sketch of typical pithouse structure.

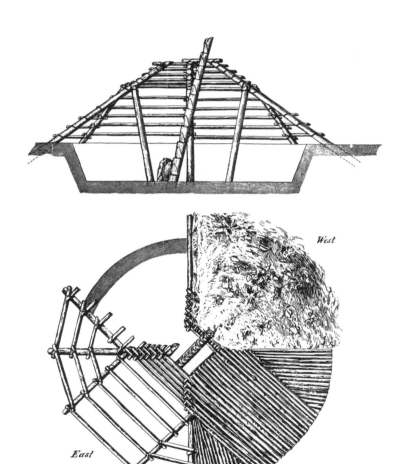

West

East

make reference to 'hot ash and melted rock' in the Stikine River country, from about two thousand years ago to historic time.

On the far northern west coast were Eskimo and Indian communities side by side, but no linguistic relationship of Meso or later times exists between them. In fact, many west coast tribes are enigmatic, in that a few thousand years ago their culture and language seem to appear from nowhere,—they have no similarity to those of other groups. They may have been Proto-Athapascans who branched off, as the Tlingit obviously did, at a sufficiently early time to fully isolate their traditions and speech.

The Indians of the central and southern west coast continued to advance a way of life that began in Palaeo-times. And the interior plateaux of British Columbia were now home to a diversity of people that suggests a long and complex history of varied migrations. A 'pithouse' style of dwelling and preponderant reliance on fishing were almost universal, but their group traits, burial habits and artifact types were not. The pithouse sites, also common to the west coast, range from single-family locations or villages of a dozen dwellings in the Okanagan, to communities of well over a hundred houses in other areas. They vary greatly in size as well, and ranking seems to have been a distinct factor in these societies. Many of the houses as early as five thousand years ago had interior partitioning; some were obviously intended to accommodate more than one family, indicating a system of communes or collective living.

*Plate CV. Buffalo jump drive lines.*

On the plains the buffalo hunts now reached a highly systematic pitch, almost to approach 'ranching' on the part of the Indians. Communal groups of two or three villages would band for the fall and spring 'roundups'. Traps and corral-like 'pounds' were used, but the buffalo *'jumps'* yielded the most reliable source of assured food. Some were surprisingly elaborate, with 'drive lines' constructed of stone or brush, narrowing in from a starting point as much as twenty miles distant. The converging herd of animals that finally poured over the cliff at the 'jump' often numbered in the thousands, piling up an unbelievable mass of carnage at the bottom. One of the best known of these sites, the 'Old Women's Buffalo Jump' near High River, Alberta, had been in annual use from Meso-times into the eighteenth century.

The tipis of the seasonal hunting village were set up nearby, usually on a stream terrace. After the drive the work of butchering would begin, and of drying meat and making pemmican and buffalo robes for winter supply. There are many signs that most of the later Plains Indian cultures began in this period; remnants of their ritualisms are found,—stone cairns, medicine wheels and ceremonial encampments; and the first plains ceramics appear at about 2,000 B P.

By twenty-five hundred years ago, wanderers from the eastern woodlands had spread into Southern Manitoba. Their more advanced technology quickly influenced the earlier inhabitants, bringing ceramics, better weapons, and customs which have remained almost to the present. Farther north, the *Shield Archaic Tradition* identifies with similar cultures in

180

*Plate CVI. Famous 'Head-Smashed-In' buffalo jump in Alberta.*

*Plate CVII. A medicine wheel on the western plains.*

Northern Ontario. The same Algonkian speakers populated the entire 'northern woodlands' zone of Canada, moving from east to west into Manitoba and Saskatchewan.

The *Old Copper Culture* of the eastern woodlands dates from 7,000 B P or earlier, and occurs throughout most of the Meso-Indian Period. Only one relic of it has ever turned up in Alberta, but in Manitoba they are numerous. Moving north, the same source was probably responsible for the items that Hearne found in use by the Copper Eskimos, rather than the 'coppermine' for which he searched in the territories. The people who made the copper implements came from the South and East, and in all cases the material itself, because of its almost total purity, could only have been obtained from the Lake Superior surface deposits.

Some Algonkians who had settled in the East learned a primitive agriculture from the Iroquois, growing corn, beans and pumpkins. They appear to have been traditionally exploited by the more advanced Iroquoian-speakers,—without question they absorbed many of that nation's customs and artifact-types. The cultural evidences of the Iroquois themselves are found in all time levels from Palaeo-Indian to present. Before 5,000 B P, large numbers of a people that American archaeologists have named *Laurentians,* migrated north and east to the Great Lakes country. They mingled with the *Lamokans* who were already there; coupled with the effects of the Altithermal, these movements probably had a great deal to do with the forming of the Iroquoian language group.

In these eastern regions a higher culture was evident before 2,000 B P, and is still obvious today in differences of life-style between the eastern tribes and others. The democratic 'Iroquois League' was formed, complete with voting power for women, and the aristocracies of the hereditary sachems. In the far West, another aristocratic culture was taking shape as the coastal tribes, living an idyllic life in the midst of plenty, turned their imagination toward the arts and a complicated structuring of 'rank' societies.

The villages of the Iroquoian people were highly organised. Their longhouses were elaborate and their ceramics, dating from 4,000 B P, often include vessels large enough to feed a band from a meal prepared over one fire. As with some western tribes, both factors are suggestive of communes or clan living.

Two thousand years ago, the Canadian Indian showed much promise of engendering a civilisation equal to that of the Mayas or Incas. But its citizens died out, weakened by ease of living and little challenge. The generations who took their place gradually slowed the momentum of the rising societies; and at the end of the Meso-Indian Period they were as hardy and resourceful,—as simple and free, as they had been five thousand years before.

## The Neo-Indian Period

In the preceding six thousand years the basic language stocks of Canada had become well defined. Salishan, Siouan, Athapascan, Algonkian, Iroquoian and Eskimoan had long ceased to share any resemblance. Tlingit and Kootenaian were probably earlier offshoots of Athapascan, and the origin of Haida, Tsimshian and Waukeshan is obscure; all three are in the Pacific West and could have been a Meso-time separation from the Salishan tongue.

*Plate CVIII. West Coast Village.*

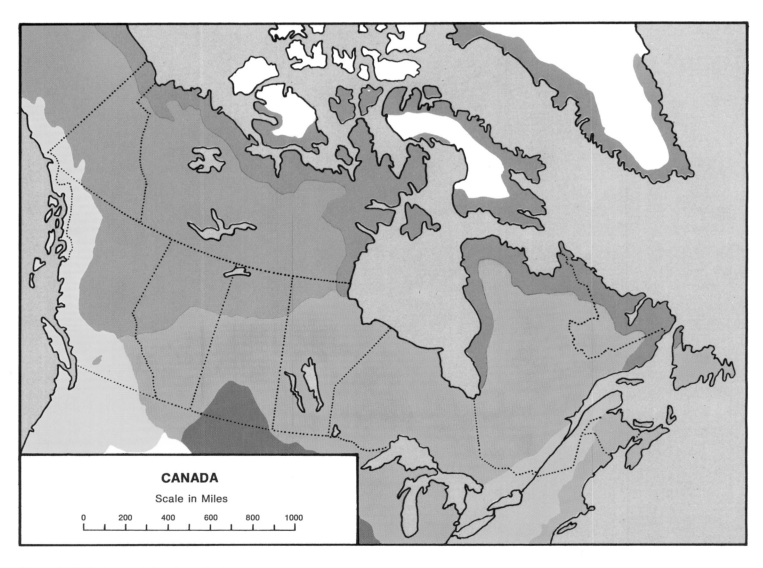

*Figure XXIX. Areas of the six major language-groups.*

Before the opening of the thousand year Neo-Indian Period the further divisions had begun, toward the profusion of almost ninety sub-languages and dialects which were to distinguish the Canadian tribes. About 1500 B P the two current main-stocks of Eskimo had separated. *Inyupik* is spoken from Norton Sound to Greenland, and west to the Diomedes. *Yupik* is the language of Western Alaska and the west coast islands. Then, by a thousand years ago the *Indian* tongues and tribal sub-groups are discernible, and the total pattern probably varied little from the following 'family-tree' that exists to-day.

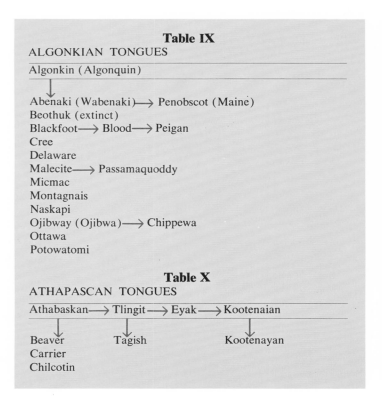

### Table IX
ALGONKIAN TONGUES

Algonkin (Algonquin)

↓

Abenaki (Wabenaki)⟶ Penobscot (Maine)
Beothuk (extinct)
Blackfoot⟶ Blood⟶ Peigan
Cree
Delaware
Malecite⟶ Passamaquoddy
Micmac
Montagnais
Naskapi
Ojibway (Ojibwa)⟶ Chippewa
Ottawa
Potowatomi

### Table X
ATHAPASCAN TONGUES

Athabaskan⟶ Tlingit ⟶ Eyak⟶ Kootenaian

↓ ↓ ↓

Beaver    Tagish         Kootenayan
Carrier
Chilcotin

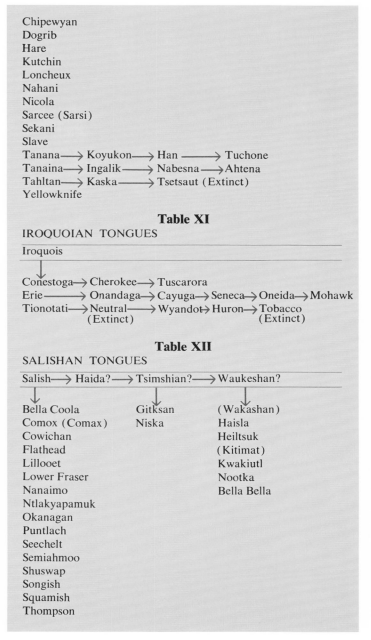

Chipewyan
Dogrib
Hare
Kutchin
Loncheux
Nahani
Nicola
Sarcee (Sarsi)
Sekani
Slave
Tanana⟶ Koyukon⟶ Han ⟶ Tuchone
Tanaina⟶ Ingalik⟶ Nabesna⟶Ahtena
Tahltan⟶ Kaska⟶ Tsetsaut (Extinct)
Yellowknife

### Table XI
IROQUOIAN TONGUES

Iroquois

↓

Conestoga⟶ Cherokee⟶ Tuscarora
Erie⟶ Onandaga⟶ Cayuga⟶ Seneca⟶ Oneida⟶ Mohawk
Tionotati⟶ Neutral⟶ Wyandot⟶ Huron⟶ Tobacco
       (Extinct)               (Extinct)

### Table XII
SALISHAN TONGUES

Salish⟶ Haida? ⟶ Tsimshian? ⟶ Waukeshan?

↓ ↓ ↓

Bella Coola        Gitksan        (Wakashan)
Comox (Comax)      Niska          Haisla
Cowichan                          Heiltsuk
Flathead                          (Kitimat)
Lillooet                          Kwakiutl
Lower Fraser                      Nootka
Nanaimo                           Bella Bella
Ntlakyapamuk
Okanagan
Puntlach
Seechelt
Semiahmoo
Shuswap
Songish
Squamish
Thompson

**Table XIII**

SIOUAN TONGUES

Sioux ⟶ Gros Ventre

⟶ (down arrow)

Assiniboine ⟶ Stony
Hidatsa
Mandan (extinct - Dakotas)
Winnebago

**Table XIV**

ESKIMOAN TONGUES

Eskimo ⟶ Aleut

Inyupik ⟶ Central Eskimo ⟶ Greenland Eskimo
Yupik ⟶ Alaska Eskimo

*Plate CIX.*

The Eskimo's habits again changed but little; if anything, his hunting skills advanced, and evidence of larger dwellings is found,—summer houses over twenty feet long which appear to have been multi-family establishments. At about 1000 B P the *Thule Culture,* (directly ancestral to the modern Eskimo,) begins in Alaska to spread eastward, still maintaining the traditional Eskimo territories.

The Indians of the Pacific Coast had brought their artistic cultures to a peak; their art and artifacts are among the finest found anywhere on Earth, far surpassing mere craftsmanship. But ecological wealth and easy living had told on the character of their high societies. A form of slavery was common, and the potlatch, famous primitive concept of 'one-upmanship,' often degenerated into a wanton orgy of destruction and waste.

In the British Columbia Interior the customs of the emerging tribes were often heavily related to the salmon; groups with access to the attractive food supply usually adjusted their economies to it, and many settlements varied with the seasons, from spring fishing sites to winter pithouse communities.

The influence of human patterns in the Kootenays seems to come downstream from the Columbia Plateau. In the Columbia Mountains, (the Monashees and Selkirks,) the villages were numerous. On the Canadian Plateau, (the Fraser region,) they were larger, with evidence of a rank system of chiefs, slaves and commoners, which may have accrued to them from the not-distant coastal tribes.

Life on the great plains still hinged on the buffalo,

*Plate CX.*

*Carving of the Salishan tribes.*

188

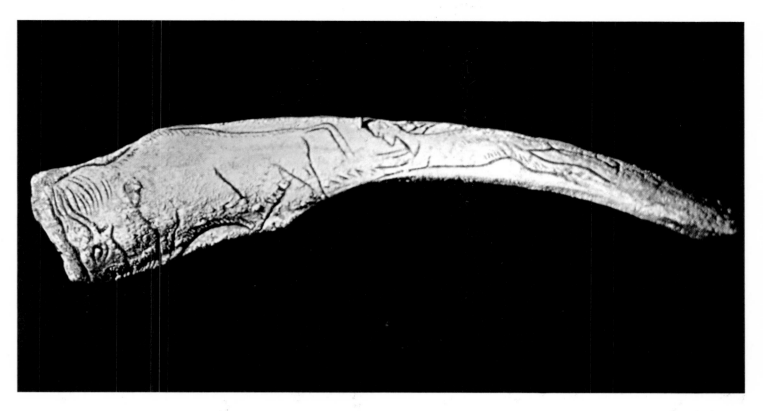

*Plate CXI. Plains carving.*

*Plate CXII. Carving, Eastern Woodlands.*

189

Plate CXIII. 'Tipi-rings,' circles of rocks which mark the locations of plains encampments.

Plate CXIV. Travois trails still remain from Meso and Historic Periods, when dogs, and later horses, were used as beasts of burden.

and the population 'explosion' held its pace. The earlier inhabitants were joined by migrating Blackfoot,—Algonkian speakers from the North and East. Leisure and ritualism hand in hand, continued to evolve a complicated system of cults and 'degrees.' And now for the first time in history before white contact, we see the Indian killing more than he needed. The winter was long and hard, and his one concern in the buffalo drives was to have enough food to weather through. *Too much* presented no problem, and the many thousands of these animals slaughtered in excess of his need, were simply left to rot at the bottoms of the jumps. The attitude of the plains hunter was not necessarily irresponsible; his lack of transportation made him a *localised* resident,—he did not know where the buffalo came from, but only that they existed in countless millions. There seemed no end to them, and it never occurred to the Indian that the supply could be exhausted. Even at that, his annual kill probably did little to halt the growth of the enormous bison herds.

The swelling populations of the eastern woodlands were partially integrated, at least in custom. Their habits show continuous sign of interaction, from the southern Iroquois territory to the lands of the Algonkian in the North and East. Evidences of the *Old Copper* and later cultures, are common in part to all tribes including the Beothuks of Newfoundland. In more northern Ontario and Quebec there was heavy hunting penetration, but little permanent living. The camp sites suggest that family and clan groups, over considerable time depth may have dispersed each winter, to assemble in villages during the summer months.

The settlement patterns of the great western continent had become a bewildering assemblage of unrelated occupancies. Intercommunication of the major regional groups was rare, and with each passing century rendered more improbable by the diverging languages. The Meso-time spectre of an ocean-to-ocean hierarchy had vanished, and the societies that might have structured it, decayed. North America, like early Europe with her kaleidoscope of tongues and cultures, was totally at the mercy of any advanced and disciplined invader.

Had there been any continental unity among the native people, the white man could no more easily have 'taken' their lands than he could have conquered China. He lacked the means of mass transport, and his weapons would not have been adequate to their numbers. Though his bigotries and beliefs might still label them 'heathen' or 'savage,' he would needs have arrived as a diplomatic visitor and hopeful immigrant, requesting permission to enter.

And hospitality was ever the Indian's way! Had the advantage been his in the turn of history, it seems most likely that his 'paleface brother' would have been welcomed—and might well have brought the technologies and faiths of Europe to the New World as contributor, and not as master.

*Plate CXV. With the coming of horses, the 'Chase' method
of buffalo hunting replaced the communal drives.*

## The Historic Period

In 'historic' time, (roughly the last five hundred years,) the European influx admittedly dwarfs all other events in national development. But the far-reaching ethnic relationships that resulted are left to the next phase in this series, the histories of the native tribes of Canada. Here let it suffice to say that their life-style was almost instantly altered in total, and their own cultural formations abruptly terminated.

For the piecemeal societies of the Indian there was no defence against the white man's devices or his ever-increasing numbers. And neither Eskimo nor Indian had any hereditary resistance to his diseases. But the deadliest adversary of all *was the white man's economy*. Once exposed to the European's trade goods, his tools and weapons, the Indian could not live without them. And the newcomer's insatiable appetite for furs and land, were the only means by which he might obtain them. Tribal wars, never before common, now became numerous; territories were coveted, because more land meant more fur and more trading power. And the tribe *without* trading power was soon overrun by its neighbours who possessed metal axes and firearms.

There is some popular belief too, that the first supply of horses came from the fur trader. The early traders in Canada had only boats, and the Indians of the western plains were fully equestrian before they arrived. The horse was re-introduced to Central America by the Spanish, and particularly by the armies of Cortés, whose forces included well equipped cavalry.

The true reason for their extinction here after the Ice Age, is still unknown. As a grazing mammal the horse re-adapted quickly and easily to the Americas, his spread to the northern regions hastened by human use. The wild herds, offshoots of animals that strayed or escaped from Spanish *remudas,* multiplied and migrated north from Mexico. Southern Indians captured and tamed many of them, but also acquired them from the whites,—sometimes in trade and more often by simply driving them off in raids. The Indian did not recognise the white man's law, and indeed at that time had no obligation to do so. His attitude to environment, and his traditions, held the products of Nature to be the property of all,—he made no acceptance of the European's 'ownership' of the horse.

In the North, where the white man had not yet been seen, horses were obtained through barter and warfare among the tribes, and from the herds of wild mustangs which now roamed the West.

In British Columbia, neither coastal nor interior patterns changed markedly from the preceding period, until the evidences of white trade influence. The villages of the plateaux became smaller, probably after the acquisition of horses, and single pithouse sites became common. 'Ranking' seems even more apparent than before, indicating a further decay of structural society, and on the Canadian Plateau there was a population decrease of some 40% in historic time.

193

*Plate CXVI. Ruins of an Historic Period longhouse.*

*Plate CXVII. A plains tipi.*

194

*Plate CXVIII. Rock petroglyph, plains.*

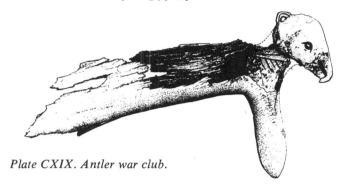

*Plate CXIX. Antler war club.*

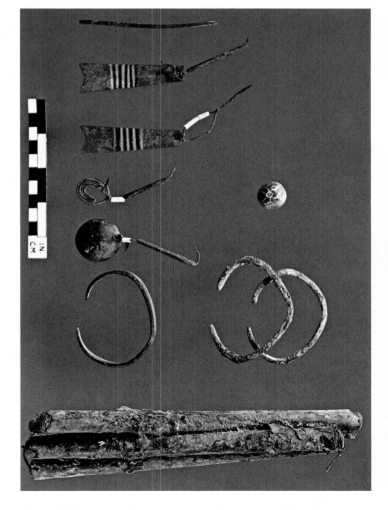

*Plate CXX. Personal ornaments made from 'trade' copper.*

*Plate CXXI. Rock petroglyph, B.C. Interior.*

*Plate CXXII. Red ochre pictograph.*

*Plate CXXIII. Red ochre pictograph.*

The Plains Indian quickly gravitated to the new life afforded by trade goods. Firearms and metal, by way of tribal exchanges, reached him before the fur traders themselves. Communal hunting was discarded,—the buffalo could now be pursued on horseback and shot with rifles. With it their interdependence vanished, and their equality. By 1800, the buffalo jumps had been abandoned, to be replaced by the 'chase.' And since a pedestrian is not capable of competing with a mounted hunter,—there were now 'rich' and 'poor' Indians on the plains.

The 'contact' events of the East, where the Europeans maintained their heaviest concentration, were even more decisive. The Iroquois of the League held their ground for a time, and were to have a long and colourful part in the white man's conflicts. But the Algonkian groups often gave way with little resistance to the encroaching newcomers. The proud and peaceful Hurons suffered such debilitation of their economy that they came to be known by the fierce, arrogant core of the Iroquois, as "dog-eaters."

\*     \*     \*

The paths of the first Canadians are reconstructed with growing clarity, as archaeology retraces their footsteps. But the secret of true accuracy lies with the Canadian Indian. Sadly, it is buried in cultures that included no recording of his heritage, and the handed down memories of a people will not long endure if they are not written. Hundreds of centuries, a thousand generations,—perhaps many more, had come and gone since his forebears first set foot on Canada's soil; as the generations passed the story dimmed, and a nation 'forgot' whence they came.

It has been estimated that before the Historic Period the native populations of North and Central America numbered over forty million, of which several million were in Canada. Presently, the Canadian total of Indian, Eskimo and Aleut combined, is less than three hundred thousand.

In the continental history of North America, her peopling by Europeans has proven the first and most vital factor to later prominence as a world power. For the Indian it was the death blow to his society,—the terminal disaster of his existence as a nation and his more-than-twenty thousand year evolution in the Western World.

*Plate CXXIV.*

196

*"And those who husbanded the golden grain,*
*and those who flung it to the winds like rain,*
*alike to no such aureate Earth are turned*
*as, buried once, men want dug up again."*

(KHAYYAM, CIRCA 900 BP)

# Appendices

# ACKNOWLEDGEMENTS

## Appendix I

The completion of this first volume in *The Romance of Canadian History,* is due in substantial part to the help of many; and to the fact that Canadian academic disciplines are filled with people who have an unfathomable ability and willingness,—to always fit one more request into what is often an already overtaxed agenda.

The text of *Years And Years Ago* was reviewed by Dr. Samuel J. Nelson, Professor of Geology and author of *The Face of Time;* the *Quaternary Period* chapters were read by Dr. Brian Reeves, (Archaeology,) at the University of Calgary; to both I am indebted for their suggestions, and to Dr. Nelson in particular for his generosity and patience throughout the entire research phase.

Special contributions to archaeological content and graphics, were made by L. A. Lahren and A. H. Stryd. Robert Dene Lacey created much of the original graphic material for the book, and the American Museum of Natural History donated many visual pieces from their collection. I am grateful to the Geological Survey of Canada for both factual aid and illustrations, and to Darlene Lacey and Irene Clevering for manuscript assistance.

Other consultants as well, are listed below; to all of these people and organisations, who have freely given advice and facility which would have been impossible to purchase, I wish to record my thanks and my respects.

Robert MacDonald.

Dr. Earl Brabb, United States Geological Survey. Alaskan geology.

T. P. Chamney, Geological Survey of Canada. Palaeontology.

Dr. Richard Forbis, University of Calgary. Archaeology.

Dr. C. R. Harington, National Museum of Natural Sciences.

Dr. L. V. Hills, University of Calgary. Quaternary geology.

Miss Helen B. Jones, American Museum of Natural History. Photography.

David Keenlyside, University of Calgary. Archaeology.

Dr. Jane Kelley, University of Calgary. Archaeology.

Dr. A. Levinson, University of Calgary. Geology.

Dr. V. J. Okulitch, Dean of Science, University of British Columbia. Astronomy, geology.

Dr. Wm. Poole, Geological Survey of Canada. Geology.

Dr. J. R. Prescott, University of Calgary. Physics.

Dr. N. W. Rutter, Geological Survey of Canada. Quaternary geology.

Dr. W. E. Taylor Jr., National Museum of Man.

Dr. R. Thorsteinsson, Geological Survey of Canada. Arctic Geology.

Dr. J. T. Wilson, Principal, Erindale College, University of Toronto. Geology.

# SELECTED REFERENCES AND RESEARCH SOURCES

## Appendix II

*Alberta, a Natural History*
Hardy. Hurtig, Edmonton, 1967.

*American Antiquity*
Salt Lake City, series publications.

American Museum of Natural History,
New York City.

*Atlas of Canada*
Dept. of Energy, Mines and Resources. Queen's Printer, Ottawa 1957.

*The Bering Land Bridge*
Hopkins, (editor). Stanford University Press, 1967.

*The Bernal Diaz Chronicles*
Idell, (editor). Doubleday, New York, 1956.

Canadian Archaeological Association, Toronto.

Canada, Department of Energy, Mines and Resources.

*Canadian Journals of Earth Sciences*
1968 - 1969 - 1970 Queen's Printer, Ottawa.

*Centennial History of Manitoba*
Jackson. M & S, Toronto, 1970.

*The Deep and the Past*
Ericson and Wollin. Knopf, New York, 1964.

*Early Man and Environments in North America*
University of Calgary. Students' Press, 1969.

*Encyclopaedia Canadiana*
Grolier Society, Ottawa, 1968.

*Encyclopaedia of Geomorphology*
Fairbridge. Reinhold, New York, 1968.

*Eskimo Prehistory*
Bandi. University of Alaska Press, 1969.

*Essentials of Earth History*
Stokes. Prentice-Hall, Toronto, 1966.

*Ethnographic and Archaeological Interpretation,*
Anderson. *Science,* Volume 163, Washington, 1969.

*The Evidence of Evolution*
Hotton. M & S, Toronto, 1968.

*The Evolution of Culture*
White. McGraw-Hill, New York, 1959.

*The Face of Time*
Nelson. Alberta Society of Petroleum Geologists, Calgary, 1970.

*Geological History of Western Canada*
Alberta Society of Petroleum Geologists, Calgary, 1964.

Geological Survey of Canada.

*Geology of Canada*
G S C. Queen's Printer, Ottawa, 1967.

*Geology and Economic Minerals of Canada*
G S C, fifth edition. Queen's Printer, Ottawa, 1970.

*Glacial and Pleistocene Geology*
Flint. Wiley, New York, 1957.

*The Great White Mantle*
Woodbury. Viking, New York, 1962.

The Heye Foundation, New York City.

*Historical Atlas of Canada*
University of Western Ontario. Nelson, Toronto, 1966.

*Historical Geology*
Dunbar. Wiley, New York, 1960.

*Historical Reviews of the Indian Affairs Branch*
1966 - 67 - 69. Government of Canada, Queen's Printer, Ottawa.

*The Indian and the Horse*
University of Oklahoma Press, Norman, 1955.

*The Indian Background of Canadian History*
Diamond Jenness. Queen's Printer, 1937.

*The Indians of Canada,*
Diamond Jenness. Queen's Printer, Ottawa, 1963.

*The Indian Tribes of North America*
J. R. Swanton. New York, 1953.

*Introduction to Archaeology of Alberta*
Wormington and Forbis. Denver, 1965.

*Introduction to Historical Geology*
  Moore. McGraw-Hill, New York, 1958.
*The Last Million Years*
  Coleman. University of Toronto Press, 1941.
*Life Before Man*
  Forbes. Black, London, 1959.
*The Long Death*
  Andrist. MacMillan, New York, 1964.
*Man's Rise to Civilisation*
  Farb. Dutton, New York, 1968.
*Million Years of Man*
  Carrington. Weidenfeld and Nicolson, London, 1963.
National Museums Bulletins, 1913-1969: Queen's Printer, Ottawa.
  *Anthropology Series*
  *Geological Survey Series*
  *Annual Reports*
  *Anthropology Papers*
National Museums of Canada.
*New Perspectives in Archaeology*
  Binford. Aldine, Chicago, 1968.
*Northwestern Plains Archaeology*
  Lahren and Sorrells. 1970.
*No Stone Unturned*
  Brennan. Random House, Toronto, 1959.
*Nuclear Geology*
  Faul. Wiley, New York, 1954.
*The Old Stone Age*
  Bordes. McGraw-Hill, New York, 1968.
*Our Amazing Earth*
  Fenton. Doubleday, New York, 1938.
*The Palliser Expedition*
  Spry. MacMillan, Toronto, 1963.
*Pleistocene Extinctions*
  Martin and Wright. Yale Press, New Haven, 1967.

*Prehistoric Man in the New World*
  Jennings and Norbeck, (editors). University of Chicago Press, Chicago, 1964.
*Principles of Animal Ecology*
  Albee. Saunders, Philadelphia.
*Principles of Geomorphology*
  Thornbury. Wiley, New York, 1969.
*Principles of Historical Geology*
  Stovall and Brown. Ginn, Boston, 1955.
*Principles of Invertebrate Paleontology*
  Shrock. MacGraw-Hill, New York, 1955.
*Principles of Paleoecology*
  Ager. McGraw-Hill, New York, 1963.
Public Archives of Canada, Ottawa.
*The Quaternary of the United States*
  Wright and Frey. Princeton University Press, 1965.
*Quaternary Research*
  University of Washington, 1970.
*Radiocarbon Dating*
  Libby. Science, 1961.
*Radiocarbon Reports*
  1963 - 70, G S C. Queen's Printer, Ottawa.
Royal Ontario Museum, Toronto.
*Structural Geology of North America*
  Eardley. Harper and Row, New York, 1962.
*Study of the Earth*
  White. Prentice-Hall, New Jersey, 1962.
*Ten Thousand Years*
  Manitoba Archaeological Society, 1970.
*Time, Life and Man*
  Stirton. Wiley, New York, 1963.
United States Geological Survey.
*When Buffalo Ran*
  Grinnell. University of Oklahoma Press, Norman, 1966.

# GUIDE TO ILLUSTRATIONS AND GRAPHIC CREDITS ***

**Appendix III**

205

\* *Courtesy of the Geological Survey of Canada.*

\*\* *Courtesy of the American Museum of National History.*

√ *Partially after Scheele, 1954.*

\*\*\**The author and The Ballantrae Foundation gratefully acknowledge that permissions for the reproduction of all illustrations credited, have been freely donated to the Foundation and to the series* Romance Of Canadian History, *for use in volume one,* Years And Years Ago, *and for continuing use in projects associated with the series.*

Date

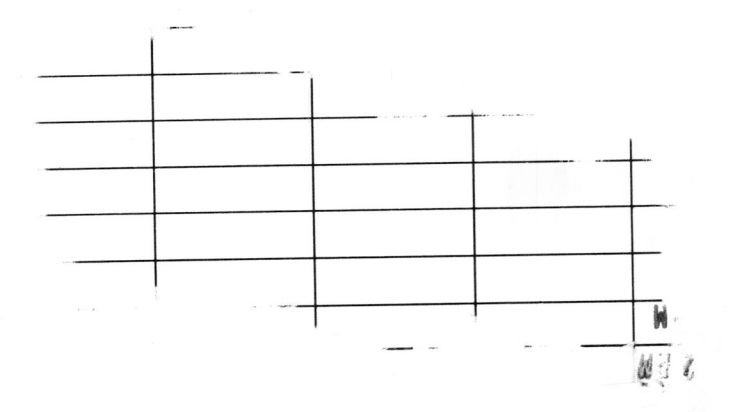